UNIT 15: WAVES

THE OPEN
UNIVERSITY

A SECOND LEVEL COURSE

PREPARED BY THE
COURSE TEAM

281: BASIC PHYSICAL SCIENCE FOR

TECHNOLOGY

UNIT 15: WAVES
UNIT 16: GEOMETRICAL OPTICS

THE
OPEN UNIVERSITY PRESS

BASIC PHYSICAL SCIENCE FOR TECHNOLOGY

Course Team

I. Boustead	(Chairman)	E. Murphy	(Technology)
P. F. Chapman	(Technology)	J. M. Richards	(Technology)
R. M. Hardman	(Designer)	J. N. Siddall	(Graphic artist)
D. A. Johnson	(Science)	J. J. Sparkes	(Technology)
A. C. Jones	(Editor)	R. Steadman	(Assessor)
S. Lewis	(Designer)	G. M. Viggars	(Course co-ordinator)
R. S. Mackintosh	(Science)	G. Wexler	(Technology)
A. Millington	(BBC)	W. Young	(BBC)

Cover illustration: *The Pancake Making Machine* by W. Heath Robinson. © Estate of Mrs J. C. Heath Robinson/Penguin books.

The Open University Press
Walton Hall, Milton Keynes, MK7 6AA

First published 1984.

Designed by the Graphic Design Group of the Open University.

Filmset by Composition House Limited, Salisbury, Wiltshire.

Printed in Great Britain by Thamesdown Litho Limited, Swindon, Wiltshire.

ISBN 0 335 17166 4

This text forms part of an Open University course. A complete list of the units of the course appears at the end of this text.

For general availability of supporting material referred to in this text please write to: Open University Educational Enterprises Ltd., 12 Cofferidge Close, Stony Stratford, Milton Keynes MK11 1BY.

Further information on Open University Courses may be obtained from: The Admissions Office, The Open University, PO Box 48, Walton Hall, Milton Keynes, MK7 6AB.

1.1

CONTENTS

Aims

The aims of this unit are:
1 To introduce the general properties of waves.
2 To show the origin of beats, interference and diffraction.

Objectives

After studying this unit you should be able to do the following:
1 Define, describe or otherwise explain the terms listed in Table A.
2 Calculate the wavelength, velocity, frequency or period of a sinusoidal wave, given the appropriate data.
3 Derive an equation for a sinusoidal wave and, given the appropriate data, assign values to the parameters.
4 Describe the origin of beating and, given the appropriate data, calculate the beat frequency.
5 Describe the vibrations that can occur in a vibrating column of air and, given the appropriate data, calculate the wavelength of the sound emitted.
6 Describe how light waves can produce an interference pattern in a double-slit experiment and, given the appropriate data, perform numerical calculations for this experiment.
7 Use Huygens' construction to determine the position of a new wavefront.
8 Describe the origin of diffraction by a single slit and, given the appropriate data, calculate the positions of maxima and minima in the diffraction pattern.

Table A   Terms introduced in this unit

amplitude	interference
angular frequency	longitudinal wave
beats	overtone
beat frequency	period
coherent sources	principle of superposition
constructive interference	Rayleigh criterion
destructive interference	resolving power
diffraction	standing wave
electromagnetic spectrum	transverse wave
electromagnetic waves	travelling wave
frequency	wavefront
fundamental wavelength	wave profile
Huygens' construction	wave tank
intensity	

1 INTRODUCTION

1.1 The occurrence of waves

If a stone is thrown into a still pool, ripples spread across the surface. But what exactly is moving? It cannot be the water in bulk because a twig floating on the water merely bobs up and down; it doesn't move bodily in the direction of the ripples. However, the fact that the twig starts to move up and down as the ripples pass indicates that the surface waves must be transporting energy; it requires energy to move the twig up and down.

This idea of waves transporting energy without bulk movement of matter is a fundamental property of all waves. Water waves may be the most familiar example, but radiant energy from the sun is transported to the earth as a waveform (electromagnetic waves) and sound energy is transported as pressure waves.

Despite the very diverse phenomena that involve wave motion, all waves possess some common properties and this unit looks at these common properties and shows how they can be used to explain some observed effects.

1.2 This week's work

There are two components to this week's work; this unit text and the associated problems in the *Problem Book*. As usual, you should work your way through the unit attempting the self-assessment questions as you come to them. At appropriate points you will be referred to the relevant questions in the *Problem Book* and ideally you should tackle them when you see the reference. If, however, you find yourself short of time, leave them until you have finished the unit. They should then act as an effective set of revision questions.

2 PERIODIC WAVES

2.1 The wave tank

The simplest way to start thinking about wave motion is to consider the behaviour of water waves, and one of the simplest pieces of apparatus that can be used to observe such waves is the *wave tank*, shown in Figure 1. This is merely a long rectangular tank filled with water. A paddle at one end is moved back and forth sinusoidally and this causes waves to move along the tank. If the paddle is moved uniformly then a series of identical waves, uniformly spaced, will travel along the tank. We will suppose that the tank is so long that any waves reflected from the far end of the tank have died out before they reach the section shown in Figure 1.

wave tank

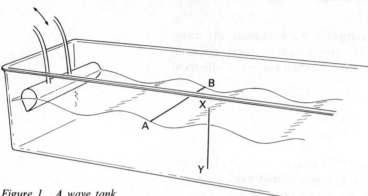

Figure 1   A wave tank

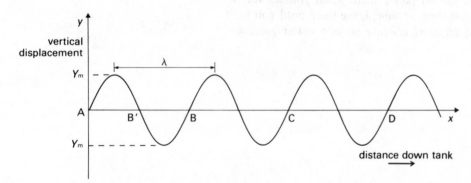

Figure 2   Schematic diagram of waves in a wave tank such as might be obtained by taking a photograph at any instant

If a camera were set up at the side of the tank and a photograph taken of the waves at any instant, it might appear as shown in Figure 2. The shape of the wave is known as the *wave profile*. If the sequence of waves is uniform, so that the wave train could be constructed by repeating a small segment, say AB in Figure 2, then the wave is said to be a repetitive or regular wave. That is, segment AB in Figure 2 is the same as segments BC, CD, and so on. These wave profiles are similar to the waveforms considered in Unit 13 except that here they are *spatially* distributed; the sinusoids are a function of *distance* rather than *time*.

wave profile

An important parameter that describes a regular wave is the wavelength λ (Greek letter lambda) shown in Figure 2. This is the distance between two adjacent identical points on the wave. Figure 2 shows it as the distance between adjacent peaks but we could equally well have chosen the distance AB. (Note that the point B′ is not the same as the point A; although the displacement is zero, B′ is on the falling side of the wave whereas A is on the rising side, so the distance AB′ is *not* a measure of wavelength.)

8

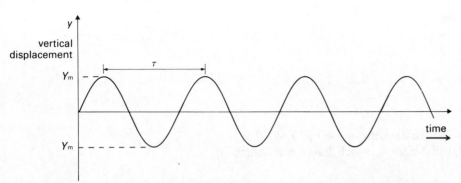

Figure 3 Vertical displacement as a function of time for periodic water waves passing a point

Now the 'snapshot' which gives rise to the graph of Figure 2 represents the profile of the wave at any instant in time. But we know that as time progresses the waves move along the tank. To follow the progress of the waves with time, suppose a vertical line is drawn on the side of the wave tank as shown by XY in Figure 1. Now suppose that we noted the position of the water surface on this line at regular time intervals. We could plot a graph of position as a function of time and obtain a graph similar to that shown in Figure 3.

Again, the graph appears as a series of regular oscillations and just as we could define wavelength when considering the waveform as a function of distance, we can now define the *period* of the wave τ (Greek letter tau) as the time interval between two identical points on the wave as shown in Figure 3.   **period**

Now if we know the distance between adjacent identical points on a wave (the wavelength) and if we know the time taken for these identical points to pass a fixed position in space (the period), then we can calculate the *velocity of the wave v.*

$$v = \frac{\text{distance between identical points on the wave}}{\text{time for identical points to pass a fixed position}}$$

$$= \frac{\text{wavelength}}{\text{period}}$$

So $v = \frac{\lambda}{\tau}.$ (1)

A more common measure of period is the *frequency of the wave f*, defined as   **frequency**
the number of waves passing a fixed point in unit time. So if the period is τ seconds, then the number of waves passing the point in one second must be $1/\tau$. So

Frequency $= f = \frac{1}{\tau},$ (2)

and equation (1) becomes

$v = \lambda f,$ (3)

or

Velocity = wavelength × frequency.

This is an important relationship that you must remember. The units of frequency are, as before, hertz (Hz), and 1 Hz corresponds to one wave passing a fixed point in one second. Hertz simply means cycles per second.

To show how equation (3) is used, the velocity of sound in air is 330 m s^{-1} (at 273 K). Middle C on a piano has a frequency of 264 Hz. Calculate its wavelength. From equation (3)

$$\lambda = \frac{v}{f}.$$

If $v = 330$ m s^{-1} and $f = 264$ Hz then

$$\lambda = \frac{330}{264} \text{ m}$$

$$= 1.25 \text{ m}.$$

SAQ 1 (Objective 2)

The velocity of radio waves (electromagnetic waves) is 3×10^8 m s^{-1}. What is the frequency (in Hz) of Radio 4, which has a wavelength of 1500 metres?

SAQ 2 (Objective 2)

The C above middle C on a piano has a frequency of 528 Hz. If the velocity of sound in air in 330 m s^{-1}, calculate:

(a) the wavelength of this note;

(b) its period.

SAQ 3 (Objective 2)

The wavelength of light from an ultraviolet light source is 365×10^{-9} m (365 nm). The velocity of light is 3×10^8 m s^{-1}. What is the frequency of this light?

2.2 Equation of a sinusoidal wave

Unit 13 showed how an alternating voltage with an instantaneous value v could be described by an equation of the form

$$v = V_m \sin \omega t, \tag{4}$$

where V_m is the maximum value of voltage or *amplitude*, ω is *angular frequency* and t is time. As shown in Unit 13, angular frequency ω is related to frequency f by the equation

amplitude

angular frequency

$$\omega = 2\pi f. \tag{5}$$

So if, for example, $f = 50$ Hz, then $\omega = 2\pi \times 50$ radians per second, or 314.2 radians per second, and equation (4) would be $v = V_m \sin 314.2\, t$.

In fact equation (4) can be used to describe *any* time-dependent sinusoidal waveform; the voltage term is simply replaced by the appropriate variable. Thus if we wished to describe a water wave such as that shown in Figure 3, where the variable is displacement y, then equation (4) would be modified to

$$y = Y_m \sin \omega t, \tag{6}$$

where Y_m is the maximum displacement (see Figure 3).

Equation (6) then is the equation of the wave describing the variation of displacement y with time t as shown in Figure 3. This equation can be written in terms of frequency or period using equations (2) and (5). So the alternative forms, which you need not remember, are

$$y = Y_m \sin 2\pi f t \tag{7}$$

and

$$y = Y_m \sin \frac{2\pi}{\tau} t. \tag{8}$$

Now let's consider the spatial wave of Figure 2. We can easily obtain an equation for this wave by comparing Figures 2 and 3. The form of the wave is identical in each figure; they are both sine waves but the time variable in Figure 3 is replaced by the distance variable x in Figure 2, and the period τ in

Figure 3 is replaced by the wavelength λ in Figure 2. So the equation for the wave of Figure 2 can be derived from equation (8) by changing t and τ to x and λ respectively. This gives

$$y = Y_m \sin \frac{2\pi}{\lambda} x. \tag{9}$$

Now the original wave varied with both time *and* distance, so the equation we are seeking should be a function of both time and distance. We can obtain this equation by combining equations (9) and (7) to give

$$y = Y_m \sin\left(\frac{2\pi}{\lambda} x + 2\pi f t\right).$$

Taking 2π out as a common factor gives

$$y = Y_m \sin 2\pi\left(\frac{x}{\lambda} + ft\right). \tag{10}$$

Here, then, is the general equation of the wave relating displacement y to both distance travelled, x, and time t. If we want to examine the motion of the wave at a fixed point (i.e. x is a constant), then equation (10) reduces to

$$y = Y_m \sin 2\pi(a + ft), \tag{11}$$

where a is a constant which corresponds to the phase angle ϕ introduced in Unit 13. As you can see from equation (11), y is simply a function of time.

Alternatively, if we want to describe a 'snapshot' of the wave at a fixed time (i.e. t is a constant), then equation (10) reduces to

$$y = Y_m \sin 2\pi\left(\frac{x}{\lambda} + b\right),$$

where b is a constant and displacement y is now just a function of distance x.

It is relatively simple to assign values to the parameters in equation (10). For example, given that the speed of sound is 330 m s^{-1}, a note of frequency 264 Hz will have a wavelength of $(330/264) \text{ m} = 1.25 \text{ m}$. So

$$\lambda = 1.25 \text{ m},$$

$$f = 264 \text{ Hz},$$

and equation (10) becomes $y = Y_m \sin 2\pi\left(\dfrac{x}{1.25} + 264t\right)$ or

$$y = Y_m \sin(5.03x + 1659t),$$

where x is measured in metres and t is measured in seconds.

The quantity Y_m^2, the square of the amplitude, is called the *intensity* of the wave and is proportional to the energy transported by the wave. That is to say, if the amplitude of a wave is double, the energy it transmits will increase by a factor of 4.

intensity

SAQ 4 (Objective 3)

Radio 2 broadcasts on the medium wave band at a frequency of 693 kHz. The speed of radio waves (electromagnetic waves) is $3 \times 10^8 \text{ m s}^{-1}$. What is the general equation describing this wave?

SAQ 5 (Objective 3)

An observer at the end of a long pier observes water waves moving in towards the shore. Wave crests pass the end of the pier at the rate of one every 15 seconds and the height between a crest and a trough is 3 metres. If the distance between adjacent crests is 35 metres, what is the general equation that describes this wave?

2.3 Longitudinal and transverse waves

So far we have used water waves as an example because they are easy to visualize. Water waves are an example of *transverse waves*; that is, the direction of vibration is at right angles to the direction of propagation. In other words, if the wave is moving along the x-direction, the oscillations are in the y- or z-directions.

transverse wave

Another example of a transverse wave is the *electromagnetic wave*. Electromagnetic waves are responsible for transmitting thermal radiation, light and radio waves. The difference between these different types of radiation is in the wavelength of the wave, and Figure 4 shows the range of wavelengths and the regions occupied by different types of radiation. This is known as the *electromagnetic spectrum*.

electromagnetic wave

electromagnetic spectrum

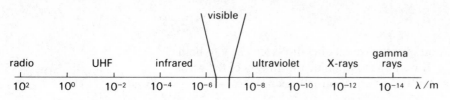

Figure 4   The electromagnetic spectrum

But what is an electromagnetic wave? It clearly cannot be a vibration in a property of a medium, such as density or pressure, because such waves can readily travel through empty space. In fact, it is the strengths of both an electric and a magnetic field that are vibrating, as shown in Figure 5, and these vibrations are at right angles to the direction of motion of the wave. In other words electromagnetic waves are transverse waves.

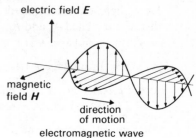

Figure 5   Electromagnetic waves

There are also waves where the direction of vibration is in line with the direction of motion of the wave. Such waves are called *longitudinal waves*. Sound waves are of this type. For example, when a tuning fork vibrates, a region of increased pressure is formed between the prongs when they move together (Figure 6a), followed by a region of low pressure when they move apart (Figure 6b). These pressure variations move away from the prongs and concentric spherical surfaces of alternating high and low pressure are formed, as in Figure 6(c).

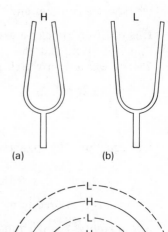

Now pressure does not have a direction since it is not a vector. However if you were to look at the movement of the air molecules, you would find them vibrating along lines at right angles to the isobars in Figure 6(c); that is, in the same direction as the direction of propagation of the sound. So sound waves are longitudinal waves.

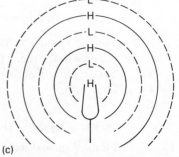

The wave nature of this motion can be made a little clearer if we plot a graph of pressure along any radial direction. This is shown in Figure 6(d) and, as can be seen, the graph is similar to that used to describe water waves. So if such a wave could be represented by a sine function, then the general equation of the wave would be of the form

$$p = p_0 + A \sin 2\pi\left(\frac{x}{\lambda} + ft\right),$$

where p is the pressure, p_0 is the mean pressure when no wave is passing, A is the amplitude, and the other symbols have the same meaning as they have in equation (10).

Figure 6   Formation of sound waves by a vibrating tuning fork. (a) When prongs are together a high pressure region H is formed between them. (b) When the prongs are apart a low pressure region L is formed between them. (c) High and low pressure variations travel away from the fork as concentric spheres. (d) Graph of pressure as a function of radial distance from the fork

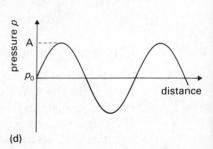

2.4 Summary of section 2

1 The velocity v of a wave is related to its wavelength λ and its frequency f by the equation $v = f\lambda$.

2 The frequency f of a wave is related to the period τ of the wave by the equation $f = 1/\tau$.

3 A periodic wave of wavelength λ and frequency f can be represented by a general equation of the form

$$y = Y_m \sin 2\pi\left(\frac{x}{\lambda} + ft\right),$$

where y is the displacement, x is the distance along the line of propagation, t is time and Y_m is the amplitude of the wave.

4 The energy transported by a wave is directly proportional to the square of the amplitude.

5 When the direction of displacement or oscillation of a wave is at right angles to the direction of propagation, the wave is called a transverse wave. Examples are electromagnetic radiation and water waves.

6 When the direction of vibration or oscillation of a wave is in line with the direction of propagation, the wave is called a longitudinal wave. An example is sound.

You should now be able to attempt questions 551–5 in the *Problem Book*.

---

3 SUPERIMPOSING WAVES

3.1 The principle of superposition

Normally when two travelling waves are superimposed one on the other, the overall vibration at any point is the sum of the individual vibrations caused by the two waves. This is known as the *principle of superposition*, and applies to all types of waves as well as many other influences. It only applies to *linear* media however; that is, to media in which the effect is proportional to the cause (e.g. media in which displacement is proportional to the force causing the displacement).

principle of superposition

The principle can be illustrated most easily by considering two single pulses of identical shape travelling in opposite directions along a piece of string, as shown in Figure 7. When the pulses are well separated, as in Figure 7(a), the overall wave profile is simply the outline of the two separate pulses approaching each other. When, however, the pulses lie on top of each other as in Figure 7(b), their effects cancel out and at that instant there is no detectable disturbance. A moment later however, they have reappeared, still travelling (Figure 7b). The momentary annihilation of both pulses did not permanently kill the travelling waves; it was merely the result of superposition.

If, on the other hand, both pulses had been deflections on the same side of the string along which they were travelling, then at the moment when they were superimposed the resultant wave profile would be the sum of the two disturbances, as shown in Figure 7(d).

When the principle of superposition applies, it is easy to calculate the form of the resulting wave caused by the application of more than one travelling wave. However, we can also carry out the reverse operation. If we are presented with a complicated wave profile, we can analyse it into a set of simpler wave profiles, such as sine waves which when added together give the original profile. We shall not be dealing with this technique of analysis in this course but we shall examine the effect of superimposing two known waves.

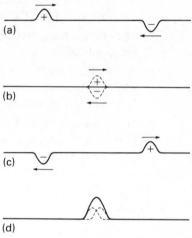

Figure 7 The principle of superposition. Two pulses travelling in opposite directions yield a resultant wave that is the sum of the two pulses. Note that when they coincide, as in (c), the resultant is zero. (d) The effect when both pulses are of the same sign

3.2 Beats

Let us first consider what happens when two waves of almost the same frequency are superimposed. Figure 8(a) shows a sine wave of period 2 s and Figure 8(b) shows a sine wave of the same amplitude but of period 2.4 s. If these two waves are superimposed the resultant wave can be found simply by adding together the graphs of Figures 8(a) and 8(b). The resultant wave is shown in Figure 8(c).

The most striking feature of the resultant wave is the variation in amplitude. It repeatedly rises and falls. This is known as the phenomenon of *beats*. It is possible to draw in an envelope which encloses the resultant wave profile and this envelope is shown by the broken line in Figure 8(c). Although Figure 8(c) shows the effect over a small time scale, the phenomenon repeats itself periodically and we can refer to a *beat frequency* as the frequency with which the envelope passes through a maximum value. From Figure 8(c) you can see that the period of the beats is 12 seconds; this is the time interval between adjacent maxima of the envelope.

beats

beat frequency

It is not difficult to calculate the beat frequency. You will see from Figure 8 that the maximum amplitude occurs when the two waves are in phase; this occurs for example between time $t = 0$ and $t = 0.5$ s, when both waves are positive and rising, and again between time $t = 12$ s and $t = 12.5$ s. In this case you can see that in the last 12 seconds, wave 1 (Figure 8a) has completed 6 cycles whereas wave 2 (Figure 8b) has completed only 5 cycles. In general, the time period for beating will be the time interval between the waves' being in phase and the next occasion when they are in phase.

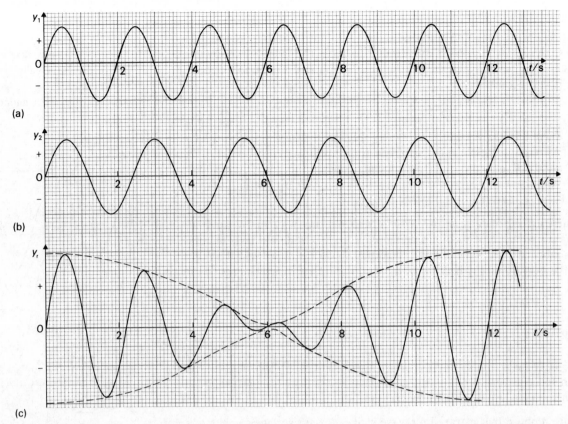

(a)

(b)

(c)

Figure 8   When two waves with slightly different periods, (a) and (b), are superimposed, the resulting wave (c) has a period intermediate between those of the two component waves but the amplitude of the resultant wave varies periodically. This is known as 'beating'

If we write f_1 as the frequency of wave 1 and f_2 as the frequency of wave 2, then in a time interval t the number of waves of type 1 that will pass a point is $f_1 t$ and the number of waves of type 2 will be $f_2 t$. If therefore

$$f_1 t - f_2 t = 1, \tag{12}$$

then t represents the time intervals between the waves' being in phase; in other words, t is the period of beating. So equation (12) becomes

$$f_1 - f_2 = \frac{1}{t},$$

and if we write f_b as the frequency of beating

$$f_b = \frac{1}{t}$$

so

$$f_b = f_1 - f_2. \tag{13}$$

That is, the frequency of beating is simply the difference in frequency of the two waves.

To illustrate that equation (13) is correct, consider the waves in Figure 8. Wave 1 has a period of 2 s so $f_1 = \frac{1}{2}$ Hz. Wave 2 has a period of 2.4 s so f_2 is 1/2.4 Hz. So, applying equation (13),

$$f_b = \left(\frac{1}{2} - \frac{1}{2.4} \right) \text{Hz}$$

$$= 0.0833 \text{ Hz},$$

and so the period for beating is $1/f_b = (1/0.833)$ s, which is 12 s. As can be seen in Figure 8(c) this is the time interval between the maximum intensities.

SAQ 6 (Objective 4)

Two sine waves of equal amplitudes but with time periods 1.0 s and 1.3 s are superimposed. Draw graphs similar to those of Figure 8 to show the existence of beating and verify from your graph that the period of beating is 4.3 seconds.

One very common use of beats is in tuning musical instruments. If you have ever listened to an orchestra tuning up, you will have heard the oboe play the A above middle C and the other instruments tune to this note. A musician plays the same note and alters the pitch until he can hear no beating between the note he plays and the note the oboe plays.

The occurrence of beating is also one of the reasons why many amateur orchestras sound harsh. If the notes being played by the different instrumentalists are almost correct, but not quite, then the listener hears not just the notes but also the beat frequency because of the slightly different wavelengths of the notes.

3.3 Standing waves

So far we have been considering *travelling waves*; that is, waveforms that are moving in space as time progresses. Examples are sound waves emitted by an instrument or light waves emitted by the sun.

Now let us suppose that a travelling wave strikes a rigid surface so that it is reflected. This is shown in Figure 9. The sequence of diagrams (a) shows an incident wave (solid) striking a reflecting surface. The reflected wave is shown moving in the opposite direction to the dashed wave. The diagrams are plotted at time intervals of one eighth of a period.

The resultant wave is shown by the sequence of diagrams (b), each diagram being calculated as the sum of the incident and reflected waves. The surprising feature about the resultant wave is that it does *not* progress with time. Such waves are called *standing waves*. Thus there are some points (B and D in Figure 9b) where the displacement is permanently zero. These are called *stationary nodes*. At intermediate positions the wave oscillates at different amplitudes and it is possible to draw in an envelope, as shown in Figure 9(c), which represents the limits of the oscillations at each point. The positions of the nodes are marked N and midway between the nodes are positions of maximum amplitude of oscillation. These are called *antinodes* and are marked A in Figure 9(c).

The other feature to note in Figure 9 is that the wavelength of the standing wave, λ, is the same as the wavelength of the incident and reflected travelling waves.

When we consider standing waves in practical situations, it is not necessary to describe them in terms of the travelling waves. Instead we can usually determine the positions of the nodes and antinodes by examining the physical constraints of the system. To illustrate this, the following section examines a particular case of standing waves – those occurring in an organ pipe.

travelling wave
standing waves
nodes
antinodes

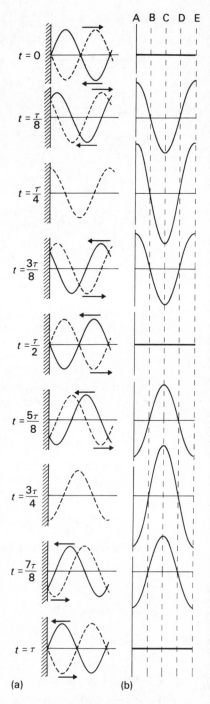

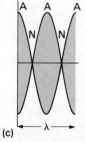

Figure 9 The production of a stationary wave as the resultant wave when an incident and a reflected wave are superimposed. The left-hand figures (a) show the incident and reflected waves. The right-hand figures (b) show the resultant wave. (c) The envelope of the standing wave, showing nodes and antinodes

3.4 The organ pipe

If you have ever blown across the top of a bottle or a tube you will know that it emits an identifiable note. The reason for this is that by blowing across the top, the air is made to vibrate and this sends a series of travelling waves along the bottle or tube. These are reflected from the end and, as a result, a standing wave is set up inside the vessel with a wavelength characteristic of the dimensions of the container; small containers emit a higher note than do larger ones. The vibrations set up by blowing cover a very wide spectrum of frequencies and wavelengths but only those which will 'fit' into the dimensions of the container will form standing waves.

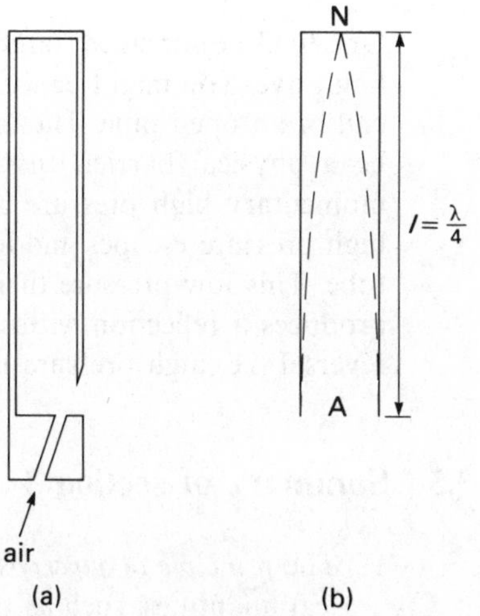

This phenomenon is the basis of the operation of an organ pipe. Figure 10(a) shows a section through a closed organ pipe. Air is blown through a tube onto a shaped hole at the bottom of the tube to cause vibrations of the air. The *fundamental wavelength* emitted by such a tube can be calculated using the simplified diagram of Figure 10(b). Air at the closed end of the tube cannot vibrate because it is in contact with the solid end. This must therefore be the position of a node; that is, a region of no vibration in the standing wave. On the other hand, the air at the open end of the pipe is free to vibrate and so this forms an antinode, or position of maximum vibration.

So the simplest waveform that can be fitted into such a tube is shown by the dashed lines in Figure 10(b). If the length of the tube is l, then clearly

$$l = \frac{\lambda}{4},$$

where λ is the wavelength of the note emitted by the pipe. So a tube of length 1 m would emit a note of wavelength 4 m.

However, other vibrations are also possible in an organ pipe. Figure 11 shows the permitted vibrations. In each case, there is always a node at the closed end and an antinode at the open end. These vibrations at higher frequencies than the fundamental are the counterpart of the harmonics in a stretched string and are usually referred to as *overtones*. For a closed pipe the pipe length is always an odd number of quarter wavelengths.

So for a closed pipe of length 1 m the three overtones shown in Figure 11 will have wavelengths of $\frac{4}{3}$ m, $\frac{4}{5}$ m and $\frac{6}{7}$ m.

SAQ 7 (Objective 5)

A closed pipe of length 50 cm vibrates so that it emits the fundamental and the first overtone. Calculate the frequencies of these two notes if the speed of sound is 330 m s^{-1}.

If an organ pipe has both ends open to the air, the mode of vibration changes because the air at both ends of the tube is now free to vibrate and hence form antinodes. Figure 12 shows the fundamental mode of vibration and the first two overtones produced in an open pipe. The important feature to note is that the wavelengths in an open pipe are different from those of a closed pipe of the same length. Thus for a pipe of length 1 m, the wavelength of the sound emitted when one end is closed is 4 m (see Figure 10), but when both ends are open the wavelength is 2 m.

SAQ 8 (Objective 5)

A closed organ pipe of length 1 m sounding its fundamental produces the same note as an open pipe sounding its first overtone. What is the length of the open pipe?

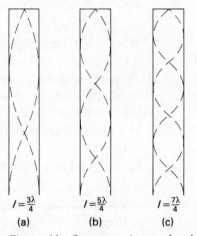

Figure 10 (a) Section through a closed organ pipe. (b) Representation of the organ pipe as a closed container, showing the position of the node (N) and the antinode (A) when sounding its fundamental note

Figure 11 Overtones in a closed organ pipe of length l

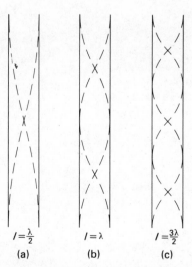

Figure 12 The open organ pipe. (a) Fundamental mode of vibration. (b) and (c) are the first two overtones. Note that both ends of the tube form antinodes

17

One final point; since standing waves are produced by the reflection of travelling waves you might be wondering how it is that waves can be reflected at the end of an open pipe. The answer is that a reflecting surface does not have to be a physical barrier. In the case of sound waves, a closed end reflects a momentary high pressure as a high pressure. At an open end, however, the high pressure escapes and leaves a momentary low pressure at the end of the tube. This low pressure then travels back down the tube. Hence a closed end produces a reflection with no phase change and an open end causes a phase reversal (i.e. high pressure is reflected as low pressure and *vice versa*).

3.5 Summary of section 3

1   The *principle of superposition* states that the result of combining two physical quantities, such as two vibrations, can be obtained by adding the two quantities as if they remained independent.

2   When two waves of slightly different frequency are superimposed the amplitude and hence the intensity periodically rises and falls. This is known as *beating*.

3   The *frequency of beating* f_b is related to the frequencies of the two waves causing the effects, f_1 and f_2, by the equation

$$f_b = f_1 - f_2.$$

4   When a travelling wave is reflected back along itself, it produces a standing wave.

5   There are some points on a standing wave which experiences no displacement. These are the *nodes*. The positions of maximum displacement are called *antinodes*.

6   In a closed organ pipe, the closed end forms a node and the open end an antinode.

7   In an open organ pipe, both ends form antinodes.

You should now be able to attempt questions 556–60 in the *Problem Book*.

---

4 INTERFERENCE

4.1 The principle of interference

Suppose two separate sources generate waves which are identical in all respects. That is, they are in phase and have the same wavelength and amplitude. If waves from these two sources arrive at the same point, what would an observer standing at that point detect?

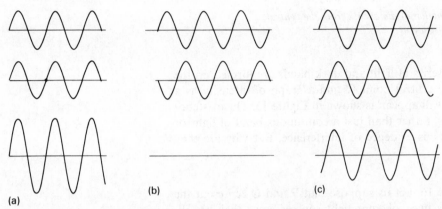

Figure 13 Interference effects. (a) Constructive interference. (b) Destructive interference. (c) The situation intermediate between the extremes of (a) and (b)

According to the principle of superposition, the resultant wave is the sum of the individual waves. So if the waves arriving at the point are in phase, as in Figure 13(a), they will reinforce each other and produce a resultant wave of the same wavelength as the incident waves but of double the amplitude. On the other hand, if the waves are out of phase by π radians, as in Figure 13(b), their effects cancel and the observer detects nothing. The intermediate case, when the waves are out of phase but by an angle of less than π radians, is shown in Figure 13(c). Here the observer will detect a resultant wave with an amplitude somewhere between the extremes of Figures 13(a) and 13(b).

Sources which produce waves which are identical in all respects and which are in phase with each other are called *coherent sources*, and when waves from two such sources fall on a point their effect is referred to as *interference*. If, as in Figure 13(a) the waves reinforce each other, the effect is said to be one of *constructive interference* and when their effects cancel as in Figure 13(b), the phenomenon is referred to as *destructive interference*.

coherent source
interference

constructive interference
destructive interference

4.2 The double-slit experiment

One of the first demonstrations of interference using light waves was the double-slit experiment devised by Thomas Young at the beginning of the nineteenth century. The apparatus he used is shown schematically in Figure 14. A light source A behind a single slit provides what is essentially a point source of light. The light chosen is monochromatic; that is, it emits only a single wavelength. Such a source might be a sodium discharge tube which emits almost all of its light in the wavelength 589×10^{-9} m (589 nm). This source illuminates a pair of slits, C in Figure 15, which are typically less than 1 mm apart. Since the illumination on the two slits has come from the same source, it will be coherent. A flat screen is placed at D, where the distance d in Figure 14 is typically 1 metre. In more modern experiments the plate D would be a photographic plate so that a permanent record could be obtained.

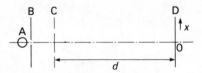

Figure 14 Schematic diagram of Young's double-slit experiment. See text for explanation

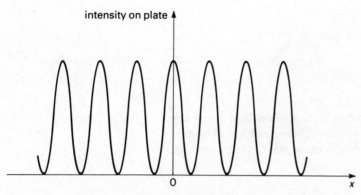

Figure 15   Light intensity as a function of distance x from the central axis in the Young's double-slit experiment

With such an arrangement, a series of light and dark bands are formed on the screen D on either side of the central point O and a graph of intensity as a function of distance x from O will appear as shown in Figure 15. The existence of these light and dark regions, rather than just a continuous band of light or a simple image of the two slits, is evidence of interference. But why are they formed?

To answer this, look at Figure 16. Let us suppose that P and Q represent the two slits and that they act as two coherent light sources since they are illuminated by the same source. At point O on the screen, equidistant from both sources, the waves will be in phase and so constructive interference will occur. So a light band will appear at O as shown in Figure 15.

However, when we consider light falling at a point R in Figure 16, the light from source P has to travel a distance PR, whereas light from source Q must travel the greater distance QR. If the path difference (QR − PR) is an integral number of wavelengths, the waves will still be in phase and constructive interference will occur. However, if the path difference (QR − PR) is equal to an odd number of half-wavelengths, the two waves will be exactly out of phase (as in Figure 13b); destructive interference will then occur and a dark band will appear on the screen.

Now, although Young's double-slit experiment can be regarded as an elegant demonstration of the existence of interference in light waves, it has the added benefit of providing a means for measuring the wavelength of light.

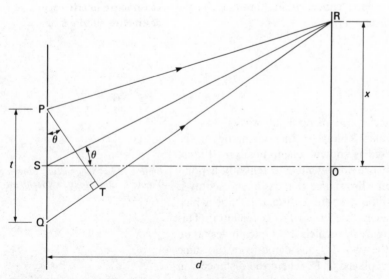

Figure 16   Path differences in the Young's double-slit experiment. (Angles are exaggerated for clarity.)

Suppose that observations are made at point R in Figure 16. Let

t = separation of the slits,

d = distance from the slits to the screen,

x = distance of R from O on the plate,

θ = angle between the axis and the observer's position (see Figure 16).

In Figure 16, T marks the point on the path QR where PR = TR. The path difference that we want to calculate is therefore QT.

Now to evaluate QT there are two approximations that can be made. These greatly simplify the calculation without introducing any significant error. These approximations arise from the fact that the angle θ is very small (usually less than 5°) so that the lines PR, SR and QR are almost parallel. As a result:

(a) the angle $P\hat{T}Q$ can be regarded as a right angle;

(b) the angle $T\hat{P}Q$ can be set equal to the angle $R\hat{S}O$.

These approximations are shown in Figure 16.

Now for triangle PQT,

$$\sin \theta = \frac{QT}{PQ} = \frac{QT}{t}. \tag{14}$$

For triangle SRO,

$$\tan \theta = \frac{RO}{OS} = \frac{x}{d}. \tag{15}$$

But for small angles (θ less than about 5°)

$$\tan \theta = \sin \theta.$$

So, combining equations (14) and (15) gives

$$\frac{QT}{t} = \frac{x}{d}$$

$$QT = \frac{xt}{d}. \tag{16}$$

If a bright fringe occurs at point R, then there must be constructive interference and this only occurs when the path difference, QT, is equal to an integral number of wavelengths. That is

$$QT = n\lambda,$$

where n is an integer and λ is the wavelength of the light. Hence equation (16) becomes

$$n\lambda = \frac{xt}{d} \tag{17}$$

for bright fringes.

To illustrate how this equation can be used, suppose a double-slit experiment is set up using monochromatic light of wavelength 589 nm (the yellow line from a sodium discharge lamp) and slits 0.5 mm apart with the slits a distance of 1 m from the screen. How far apart are the bright fringes on the screen?

Using equation (17) the nth bright fringe occurs at x_n, where

$$x_n = \frac{n\lambda d}{t}.$$

The next bright fringe occurs at x_{n+1}, and this is the $(n + 1)$th bright fringe. So

$$x_{n+1} = \frac{(n + 1)\lambda d}{t}.$$

The separation of these two fringes is

$$x_{n+1} - x_n = \frac{\lambda d}{t}(n+1) - \frac{\lambda dn}{t}$$

$$= \frac{\lambda d}{t}. \tag{18}$$

We are given these data:

$\lambda = 589 \text{ nm} = 589 \times 10^{-9} \text{ m},$

$d = 1 \text{ m},$

$t = 0.5 \text{ mm} = 0.5 \times 10^{-3} \text{ m}.$

So

$$x_{n+1} - x_n = \frac{589 \times 10^{-9} \times 1}{0.5 \times 10^{-3}} \text{ m}$$

$$= 0.001\,18 \text{ m}$$

$$= 1.18 \text{ mm}.$$

Note that equation (18) does not contain n, indicating that the separation of the fringes is constant. The numerical calculation shows that the bright fringes are separated by a distance of 1.18 mm.

In equation (18), the terms d and t can be measured, as can $(x_{n+1} - x_n)$, the separation of the fringes. Hence equation (18) can be used to determine the wavelength of the light used in an experiment.

SAQ 9 (Objective 6)

A Young's double-slit experiment is performed with ultraviolet light of wavelength 254 nm and with the screen placed 2 m from the slits. If the separation of the bright fringes on the screen is 2 mm, what is the spacing of the slits?

SAQ 10 (Objective 6)

Using the same wavelength of light and the same distance of the slits from the screen as in SAQ 9, what will be the separation of the fringes if the slits are 0.5 mm apart?

4.3 Interference in practical examples

Since sound and light are both propagated by waves, it is initially surprising to find that interference effects are not more commonly observed. Examples do however occur in nature. The most commonly observed occurrences arise when the same wave is somehow divided into two parts in such a way that the parts eventually recombine after following different paths.

For example, you may well have observed the presence of bright colours on thin oil films or on bubbles. This is an interference effect produced by the interaction of light waves reflected from the top surface of the film with those reflected from the bottom surface, as shown in Figure 17. The light reflected from the bottom surface has to travel the extra distance XYZ and this produces a phase shift in the waves. The fact that such films appear brightly coloured is because white light contains waves of many wavelengths, each corresponding to a different colour. But only some of these wavelengths will interfere constructively for a given thickness of oil film.

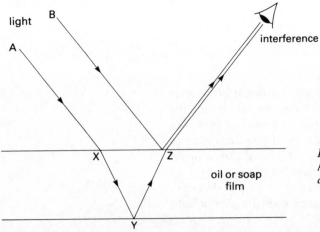

Figure 17   Interference in a thin film. Before light from A recombines with light from B, it must travel to extra distance XYZ.

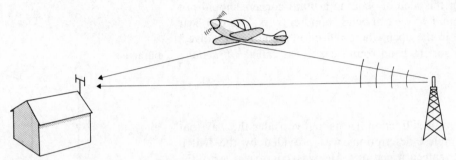

Figure 18   Interference of electromagnetic waves carrying a television signal by an aircraft

Another fairly common example of an interference effect is illustrated in Figure 18. Here the electromagnetic wave carrying a television signal is partially reflected by an aeroplane. Thus the aerial receives two signals, one directly from the transmitter, the other reflected from the plane. For some positions of the aeroplane these two signals are exactly out of phase; for other positions they are in phase, so the net signal sent to the receiver varies in amplitude as the aeroplane moves across the sky. When the waves are out of phase they do not totally cancel since the reflected wave usually has a much smaller amplitude than the direct wave. Nevertheless the variation in signal strength as the aeroplane flies over is usually clearly visible to the viewer of the television set.

4.4   Summary of section 4

1   Interference occurs when two coherent waves are superimposed.

2   Constructive interference occurs when the waves are exactly in phase.

3   Destructive interference occurs when the waves are π radians (180°) out of phase.

4   A pair of closely spaced slits illuminated by a coherent source of monochromatic light will produce an interference pattern on a distant screen. If the separation of the slits is t, the wavelength of the light is λ, and the distance of the screen from the slits is d, then a bright fringe will occur at a distance x from the axis where

$$n\lambda = \frac{xt}{d}$$

and n is any integer.

You should now be able to attempt questions 561–5 in the *Problem Book*.

5 DIFFRACTION

5.1 Introduction

Common experience seems to indicate that light travels in straight lines. After all, on a sunny day the sun casts sharp shadows. However this is not the whole truth. As long ago as 1665 Grimaldi found that the shadow of a very fine wire was much broader than expected. Furthermore, if you look back to Figure 14, the experimental arrangement for Young's double-slit experiment does not provide a direct line of sight from the light source to the point O; yet a bright interference fringe appears at point O. This seems to suggest that light can bend around corners, something that is at variance with the idea of light travelling in straight lines.

But if light is a wave motion this idea of bending around corners should not be so surprising. After all, sound waves can bend round corners; you can hear noises around a corner even in the open where reflection cannot be involved. This ability of waves of any sort to bend round corners is called *diffraction*.

diffraction

5.2 Huygens' construction

To understand the mechanism of diffraction, let us first consider the way that waves move. One of the simplest descriptions was provided by the Dutch physicist Huygens in the seventeenth century. He was concerned with the movement of a *wavefront*; that is, an imaginary line at right angles to the direction of propagation of the wave. In Figure 1, the wavefront is line AB.

wavefront

Huygens postulated that every point on a wavefront acted as a source of secondary waves. So in Figure 19, if the line AB represents a wavefront travelling with a speed v, then we can choose a series of points (say a, b, c, d, e, f) on this wavefront. Each of these points acts as a source of secondary waves, which also travel with speed v. After a time t, the positions of these secondary waves can be constructed as circles of radius vt, as shown in Figure 19. The new wavefront XY is then the line which touches all these secondary wavefronts. This technique for determining the position of the new wavefront is called *Huygens' construction*.

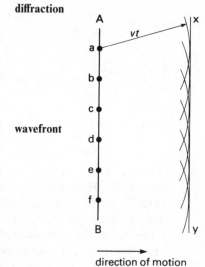

Figure 19 Huygens' construction for a plane wavefront. Wavefront AB acts as a source of secondary waves. In time t the secondary waves will have travelled a distance vt, where v is the speed of the wave and the new wavefront XY is the line touching all the secondary waves

SAQ 11 (Objective 7)

A stone is thrown into a still pond of water and causes waves to move outward in a circle. The speed of the wavefront is $1 \, \text{m s}^{-1}$. Draw the position that the wavefront will have reached one second after the stone has been dropped in, and use Huygens' construction to determine the position of the wavefront 0.5 second later.

5.3 Single-slit diffraction

One important consequence of Huygens' construction is that if a wavefront acts as a collection of sources of secondary waves, then these secondary waves may interfere with each other. Look at Figure 20. This shows a plane wavefront AB and an observer at O. Consider the two points P and Q on the wavefront. Secondary waves emitted from P and Q will arrive at the observer. Since these waves originated from the same wavefront they will be coherent; that is, they satisfy all the conditions for interference of the type observed in the Young's double-slit experiment.

Whether the observed interference at O is constructive or destructive depends on the path difference (PO − QO). If this is an integral number of whole wavelengths, constructive interference occurs. If the path difference is an odd number of half-wavelengths then destructive interference occurs.

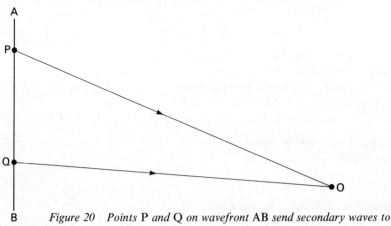

Figure 20   Points P *and* Q *on wavefront* AB *send secondary waves to an observer at* O

Now for an observer in front of an extended wavefront, waves will be received not only from points P and Q but from all the points needed to make up the wavefront AB. So for every pair of points which will produce destructive interference it is possible to choose another pair of points which will produce constructive interference. Consequently the observer does not detect any interference effect.

But what happens if the wavefront is not an extended front? Suppose that light in the form of plane wave fronts falls onto a narrow slit of width *a*, as shown in Figure 21, and is detected on a distant screen XY.

Any wavefront AB at the slit will emit secondary waves in all directions, so let's consider what is observed on the screen at a point receiving light which makes an angle θ with the line PO, where P is the midpoint of the slit.

Secondary waves from A will have to travel further than secondary waves from the point P. So there will be a path difference. We can easily calculate this path difference by making a simple assumption. Because the distance PO is very large compared to the width of the slit, the light is essentially parallel so the angle $P\hat{C}A$ is 90° and the path difference between light from A and light from P will be *x*, as shown in Figure 21.

But in triangle ACP, $AP = a/2$, $AC = x$, angle $A\hat{P}C = \theta$ and angle $P\hat{C}A = 90°$; so $\sin \theta = x/(\tfrac{1}{2}a)$, or

$$x = \tfrac{1}{2}a \sin \theta. \tag{19}$$

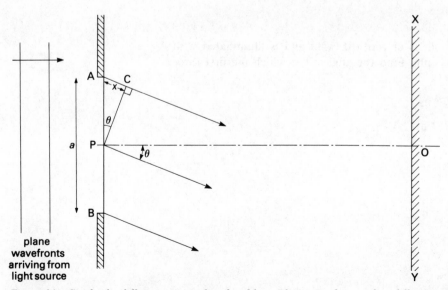

Figure 21   Single-slit diffraction at a slit of width a. Plane wavefronts after diffraction fall on screen XY

Now it is clear that for *any* point on the wavefront lying between A and P, there will always be a corresponding point on the wavefront lying between P and B for which equation (19) holds true. So equation (19) is a general equation relating the path difference x to the slit width a and the angle θ which the light makes to the line PO.

Now for *bright fringes*, the path difference must be a whole number of wavelengths, as in Young's experiment. In other words

$$x = n\lambda,$$

where n is an integer and λ is the wavelength of the light. So equation (19) becomes

$$n\lambda = \tfrac{1}{2}a \sin \theta$$

or

$$\sin \theta = \frac{2n\lambda}{a}. \tag{20}$$

This equation allows us to calculate the angle θ at which constructive interference occurs, thus producing bright bands on the screen. The integer n can take the values 0, 1, 2, 3, and so on. The intensity pattern of light and dark bands from a narrow slit turns out to be as shown in Figure 22, with a bright centre and with fringes of diminishing intensity on each side of it.

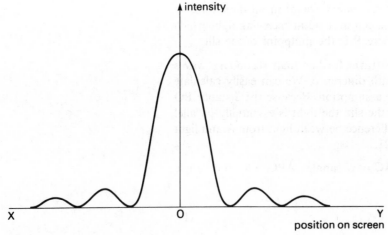

Figure 22   Intensity of the diffraction pattern produced by single-slit diffraction

For example suppose that a slit is of width 0.1 mm and is illuminated with yellow light of wavelength 589 nm. Find the angles θ at which the first three bright fringes occur.

$$a = 0.1 \text{ mm} = 0.1 \times 10^{-3} \text{ m}$$

$$\lambda = 589 \text{ nm} = 589 \times 10^{-9} \text{ m}.$$

Hence

$$\sin \theta = \frac{2n\lambda}{a}$$

$$= \frac{2 \times 589 \times 10^{-9} \times n}{0.1 \times 10^{-3}}$$

$$= 0.011\,78n.$$

When

$$n = 0, \sin \theta = 0, \qquad\qquad \theta = 0;$$
$$n = 1, \sin \theta = 0.011\,78, \qquad \theta = 0.67°;$$
$$n = 2, \sin \theta = 0.011\,78 \times 2, \theta = 1.35°.$$

SAQ 12 (Objective 8)

A single slit of width 0.05 mm is illuminated with light of wavelength 500 nm. Calculate the positions of the first four bright fringes.

Equation (19) can also be used to calculate the positions of the dark fringes. For *dark fringes*, the path difference x must be an odd number of half-wavelengths; that is $\lambda/2$, $3\lambda/2$, $5\lambda/2$ and so on. In general terms, this requirement can be written as

$$x = (2m + 1)\frac{\lambda}{2},$$

where m is any integer (i.e. 0, 1, 2, etc). So for dark fringes equation (19) becomes

$$(2m + 1)\frac{\lambda}{2} = \frac{1}{2} a \sin \theta$$

or

$$\sin \theta = \frac{(2m + 1)\lambda}{a}. \tag{21}$$

This equation allows us to calculate the angle θ at which successive dark fringes appear. To illustrate this, suppose a slit of width 0.1 mm is illuminated with light of wavelength 589 nm. Calculate the positions of the first two dark fringes.

$$a = 0.1 \text{ mm} = 0.1 \times 10^{-3} \text{ m}$$
$$\lambda = 589 \text{ nm} = 589 \times 10^{-9} \text{ m}.$$

So

$$\sin \theta = \frac{(2m + 1)589 \times 10^{-9}}{0.1 \times 10^{-3}}$$

$$= 0.005\,89(2m + 1).$$

When

$$m = 0, \sin \theta = 0.005\,89, \qquad \theta = 0.34°;$$
$$m = 1, \sin \theta = 2 \times 0.005\,89, \theta = 1.01°.$$

SAQ 13 (Objective 8)

A single slit of width 0.05 mm is illuminated with light of wavelength 500 nm. Calculate the positions of the first three dark fringes.

5.4 Resolving power

Although we have considered diffraction using the single-slit example, the effect occurs whenever light passes through any aperture or encounters any obstacle. In a great many instances the extent of the diffraction pattern is so small that it cannot be detected with the naked eye; hence the reason for saying that shadows have sharp edges, even though if we were to look very carefully we should find that this is not strictly true.

However, most optical instruments employ an aperture of one form or another and frequently create the conditions which favour the production of detectable diffraction patterns. This effect limits the quality of the image that can be produced and often limits the amount of information that can be obtained from experimental observations.

For example, suppose that you were trying to observe a star using a telescope. If diffraction effects did not exist then by scanning across the star no light would be detected until the edge of the star was reached and the light would disappear as the telescope passed the other edge. This is shown in Figure 23(a). However the star is essentially a point light-source a very long distance from the telescope aperture, so plane wavefronts arrive at the telescope aperture in much the same way as the plane wavefronts were arriving at the single slit of Figure 21. So instead of the image of the star in the telescope being a sharp point it appears as a diffraction pattern and the intensity of light during a scan across it will be as in Figure 23(b).

If the purpose of such an experiment were simply to locate the star, the position of the central maximum would provide the necessary data. However, suppose that you were trying to determine whether the star was a single star or a pair of stars close together. In the absence of diffraction effects this would be simple (Figure 24a). However, because diffraction occurs, the diffraction patterns of two stars overlap if the stars are too close together (Figure 24b) and the observed overall pattern prevents their being separated or *resolved*.

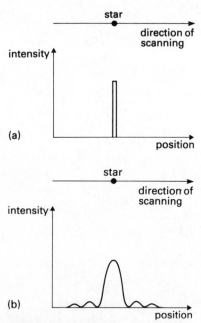

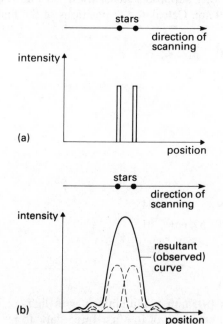

Figure 23   Detecting a star by scanning across it with a telescope. (a) The intensity pattern if no diffraction effects existed. (b) The pattern when diffraction effects are taken into account

Figure 24   Resolving two stars. (a) If there were no diffraction the stars could always be resolved, provided they were not actually coincident. (b) In practice there is diffraction, and the resultant diffraction pattern does not allow resolution of the stars if the individual diffraction patterns overlap closely

Experimentally it is found that two stars can just be resolved when the maximum of one diffraction pattern coincides with the first minimum of the second pattern as shown in Figure 25. This condition is usually referred to as the *Rayleigh criterion*. If the patterns are any closer they cannot be resolved and so the Rayleigh criterion represents the limit of resolution, or the *resolving power*, of the telescope. It can be shown that for two stars which make an angle θ at a telescope with a circular lens of diameter D

$$\theta = \frac{1.22\lambda}{D},$$

where λ is the wavelength of the light entering the telescope. From this it is clear that maximum resolution (i.e. smallest values of θ) occur when λ is short (i.e. towards the blue end of the spectrum) and when the diameter D is large. There are of course other factors which limit the resolution that can be achieved with terrestrial telescopes, such as atmospheric disturbances, but diffraction effects would dominate the performance of telescopes in space.

Rayleigh criterion
resolving power

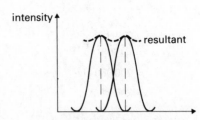

Figure 25   Rayleigh criterion for resolution. The maximum of one pattern must coincide with the first minimum of the other

5.5   Summary of section 5

1   Any point on a wavefront can be thought of as acting as a source of secondary waves. The use of this principle to show the way a wavefront advances is known as Huygens' construction.

2   For diffraction at a single slit of width a, when illuminated with light of wavelength λ, bright fringes occur at an angle θ given by

$$\sin \theta = \frac{2n\lambda}{a},$$

where $n = 0, 1, 2, 3$, etc.

3   For diffraction at a single slit of width a, when illuminated with light of wavelength λ, dark fringes occur at an angle θ given by

$$\sin \theta = \frac{(2m + 1)\lambda}{a},$$

where $m = 0, 1, 2, 3$, etc.

4   A telescope with an aperture of diameter D can just resolve two stars which emit a wavelength λ when they subtend an angle θ at the telescope where

$$\theta = \frac{1.22\lambda}{D}.$$

You should now be able to attempt questions 566–70 in the *Problem Book*.

6   POSTSCRIPT

In this unit we have concentrated on wave motion and have shown how properties such as interference and diffraction arise as a result of the wave properties of light. However, for many purposes the wave properties of light can be ignored and we can regard light as rays which travel in straight lines. This forms the basis of geometrical optics, the subject of the next unit, and the basis for the design of optical instruments.

ANSWERS TO SELF-ASSESSMENT QUESTIONS

SAQ 1

$$v = \lambda f$$

$$f = \frac{v}{\lambda}$$

$$= \frac{3 \times 10^8}{1500} \text{ Hz}$$

$$= 200\,000 \text{ Hz}$$

$$= 200 \text{ kHz.}$$

SAQ 2

(a) $v = \lambda f$

$$\lambda = \frac{v}{f}$$

$$= \frac{330}{528} \text{ m}$$

$$= 0.625 \text{ m.}$$

(b) Period $= \tau$

$$= \frac{1}{f}$$

$$= \frac{1}{528} \text{ s}$$

$$= 0.0019 \text{ s.}$$

SAQ 3

$$v = \lambda f$$

$$f = \frac{v}{\lambda}$$

$$= \frac{3 \times 10^8}{365 \times 10^{-9}} \text{ Hz}$$

$$= 8.2 \times 10^{14} \text{ Hz.}$$

SAQ 4

The relationship between frequency f, velocity v and wavelength λ is $v = \lambda f$. So $\lambda = v/f$. Here

$$v = 3 \times 10^8 \text{ m s}^{-1}$$

$$f = 693 \text{ kHz} = 693\,000 \text{ Hz.}$$

So

$$\lambda = \frac{3 \times 10^8}{693\,000} \text{ m}$$

$$= 433 \text{ m.}$$

The general equation of a wave is

$$y = Y_m \sin 2\pi\left(\frac{x}{\lambda} + ft\right)$$

$$= Y_m \sin 2\pi\left(\frac{x}{433} + 693\,000t\right)$$

$$= Y_m \sin(0.015x + 4.35 \times 10^6 t).$$

SAQ 5

The time period of the wave is 15 s. So

$$\text{Frequency } f = \frac{1}{15} \text{ Hz}$$

$$= 0.067 \text{ Hz.}$$

We are told that the wavelength is 35 m.

The height from trough to crest is twice the amplitude, so

$$\text{Amplitude} = \tfrac{3}{2} \text{ m}$$

i.e. $Y_m = 1.5 \text{ m.}$

The general wave equation is of the form

$$y = Y_m \sin 2\pi\left(\frac{x}{\lambda} + ft\right)$$

$$= 1.5 \sin 2\pi\left(\frac{x}{35} + 0.067t\right)$$

$$= 1.5 \sin(0.18x + 0.42t)$$

SAQ 6

The procedure is exactly the same as in Figure 8; the only thing to ensure is that you plot the time axes for more than 4.3 seconds to make sure that you obtain at least two maxima in the beat curve.

SAQ 7

For a closed pipe of length 50 cm (0.5 m), the fundamental wavelength λ is as given in Figure 10.

$$l = \frac{\lambda}{4}.$$

So

$$\lambda = 4l$$

$$= 4 \times 0.5 \text{ m}$$

$$= 2 \text{ m.}$$

But $v = \lambda f$. We are given that $v = 330 \text{ m s}^{-1}$, so

$$f = \frac{330}{2} \text{ Hz}$$

$$= 165 \text{ Hz.}$$

For the first overtone (see Figure 11)

$$l = \frac{3\lambda}{4}.$$

So

$$\lambda = \frac{4l}{3}$$

$$= \frac{4 \times 0.5}{3} \text{ m}$$

$$= 0.667 \text{ m.}$$

But $v = \lambda f$, and $v = 330 \text{ m s}^{-1}$. We have calculated that λ is 0.667 m, so

$$f = \frac{330}{0.667} \text{ Hz}$$

$$= 495 \text{ Hz.}$$

SAQ 8

Let l be the length of the open pipe. From Figure 12, the wavelength of the first overtone is equal to the length of the pipe, so $\lambda = l$.

For the closed pipe, the wavelength of the fundamental note is given by

$$\lambda = 4 \times \text{pipe length} \quad \text{(see Figure 10)}$$

$$= (4 \times 1)\,\text{m}$$

$$= 4\,\text{m}.$$

So l is 4 m if the first overtone of the open pipe is the same as the fundamental of the closed pipe.

SAQ 9

From equation (18),

$$\text{Distance between fringes } \Delta x = \frac{\lambda d}{t}$$

so

$$t = \frac{\lambda d}{\Delta x}.$$

We are given these data:

$$\lambda = 254\,\text{nm} = 254 \times 10^{-9}\,\text{m},$$

$$d = 2\,\text{m},$$

$$\Delta x = 2\,\text{mm} = 2 \times 10^{-3}\,\text{m}.$$

So

$$t = \frac{254 \times 10^{-9} \times 2}{2 \times 10^{-3}}\,\text{m}$$

$$= 0.000\,254\,\text{m}$$

$$= 0.254\,\text{mm}.$$

SAQ 10

From equation (18),

$$\text{Spacing } \Delta x = \frac{\lambda d}{t}.$$

We are given these data:

$$\lambda = 254\,\text{nm} = 254 \times 10^{-9}\,\text{m},$$

$$d = 2\,\text{m},$$

$$t = 0.5\,\text{mm} = 0.5 \times 10^{-3}\,\text{m}.$$

So

$$\Delta x = \frac{254 \times 10^{-9} \times 2}{0.5 \times 10^{-3}}\,\text{m}$$

$$= 0.0010\,\text{m}$$

$$= 1\,\text{mm}.$$

SAQ 11

After one second, the wave will be a circle of radius 1 m, as shown in Figure 26. In the next 0.5 s, the secondary waves generated on this wavefront will move a distance of 0.5 m. So by choosing points on the circle, it is possible to draw a series of arcs. The new wavefront will therefore be a circle of radius 1.5 m as expected.

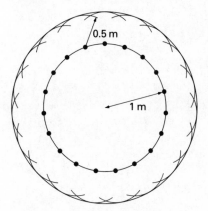

Figure 26   Answer to SAQ 11

SAQ 12

This is similar to the worked example in the text. Here

$$\lambda = 500\,\text{nm} = 500 \times 10^{-9}\,\text{m},$$

$$a = 0.05\,\text{mm} = 0.05 \times 10^{-3}\,\text{m}.$$

For bright fringes

$$\sin\theta = \frac{2n\lambda}{a}$$

$$= \frac{2 \times 500 \times 10^{-9} \times n}{0.05 \times 10^{-3}}$$

$$= 0.02n.$$

When

$$n = 0, \sin\theta = 0, \quad \theta = 0°;$$

$$n = 1, \sin\theta = 0.02, \theta = 1.15°;$$

$$n = 2, \sin\theta = 0.04, \theta = 2.29°;$$

$$n = 3, \sin\theta = 0.06, \theta = 3.44°.$$

SAQ 13

This is similar to the problem in the main text.

$$\lambda = 500\,\text{nm} = 500 \times 10^{-9}\,\text{m},$$

$$a = 0.05\,\text{mm} = 0.05 \times 10^{-3}\,\text{m}.$$

For mimimum intensity

$$\sin\theta = \frac{(2m + 1)\lambda}{a}$$

$$= \frac{500 \times 10^{-9}}{0.05 \times 10^{-3}}(2m + 1)$$

$$= 0.01(2m + 1).$$

When

$$m = 0, \sin\theta = 0.01, \theta = 0.57°;$$

$$m = 1, \sin\theta = 0.03, \theta = 1.72°;$$

$$m = 2, \sin\theta = 0.05, \theta = 2.87°.$$

UNIT 16: GEOMETRICAL OPTICS

CONTENTS

Aims

The aims of this unit are:

1 To introduce the concepts of reflection and refraction.
2 To demonstrate the properties of lenses.
3 To show how simple optical instruments are designed.

Objectives

After studying this unit you should be able do the following:

1 Define, describe or otherwise explain the meaning of the terms listed in Table A.
2 Construct ray diagrams to show the formation of shadows, the formation of eclipses and the production of the image in a pinhole camera.
3 Construct ray diagrams to show single and multiple reflections in plane mirrors.
4 Calculate angles of incidence or refraction given the appropriate data.
5 Calculate real and apparent depths given the appropriate data.
6 Calculate critical angles given the appropriate data.
7 Construct ray diagrams to locate the position and size of an image in a thin lens.
8 Derive the lens equation and, given the appropriate data, apply it in simple examples.
9 Calculate the position and magnification of the image produced by a combination of lenses.
10 Calculate the focal lengths of spectacle lenses needed to correct long and short sight.
11 Calculate object and/or image distances and magnifications in magnifying glasses and compound microscopes.

Table A   Terms used in this unit

accommodation	myopia
angle of incidence	near point
angle of reflection	objective
angle of refraction	penumbra
compound microscope	physical optics
concave lens	pinhole camera
converging lens	principal axis
convex lens	principal focus
critical angle	ray
diverging lens	ray diagram
eyepiece	real image
far point	rectilinear propagation
focal length	refraction
focus	refractive index
geometrical optics	Snell's law
hypermetropia	total internal reflection
laws of reflection	umbra
laws of refraction	virtual image
magnifying glass	

1 INTRODUCTION

1.1 Physical and geometrical optics

Unit 15 examined some of the properties of light that arise as a result of its wave nature and, in particular, highlighted the property of diffraction – the ability of light to bend around corners. However, as you will be aware from the calculations in that unit, the amount of bending is quite small and for many practical purposes it can be ignored.

This has given rise to two quite distinct study areas in optics; *geometrical optics*, which ignores the wave nature of light and assumes that light travels in straight lines, and *physical optics*, which is largely concerned with the consequences of the wave nature of light. Geometrical optics is the subject of this unit and, as you will see, despite a number of assumptions to simplify the calculations, the results provide a surprisingly good description of optical instruments, how they work and how they can be designed.

geometrical optics
physical optics

1.2 This unit's work

The main components of this unit's work are this unit text and the relevant questions in the *Problem Book*. You should study the unit in the usual manner, attempting the self-assessment questions as you come to them. At appropriate points you will be referred to the relevant questions in the *Problem Book* and these you should ideally attempt when you reach the reference.

2 RECTILINEAR PROPAGATION

2.1 Light travels in straight lines

The basis of geometrical optics is the idea that light travels in a straight line. This is known as the principle of *rectilinear propagation*. In geometrical optics we plot the paths taken by thin 'pencils' of light, or *rays*, and for light travelling in a continuous unbroken medium we assume that the path will be rectilinear. Diagrams which plot the paths taken by rays of light are known as *ray diagrams*.

rectilinear propagation
ray

ray diagrams

The most familiar evidence for rectilinear propagation is the occurrence of shadows, as shown in Figure 1. If light from a point source encounters an opaque object, a shadow with sharp edges is formed on the screen. The limits of this shadow, or *umbra*, can be determined by drawing in two rays of light from the source which just touch the edges of the object as shown. This is an example of a simple ray diagram. (Note that arrows have been inserted to show the directions of the rays; it is good to get into the habit of doing this since, as you will see later, it is important to know the directions of rays in some of the more complicated ray diagrams.)

umbra

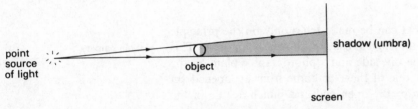

Figure 1   Light from a point source casts a shadow with sharp edges onto a screen

In practice, point sources do not exist since all light sources have finite dimensions. For a finite source the shadow is not sharp, as shown in Figure 2. A point P at the top edge of the light source will cast a sharp shadow AD. Similarly a point Q at the bottom of the source will also cast a sharp shadow BC. Intermediate points on the source will also cast sharp shadows. But as can be seen, these separate sharp shadows do not coincide. The overall effect on the screen is that the region AB receives no light and so appears as a complete shadow or umbra. But this is surrounded by regions AC and BD, which receive partial illumination. Such a region of partial shadow is known as a *penumbra*.

penumbra

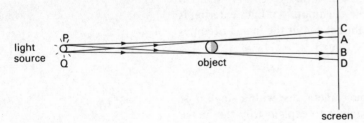

Figure 2   Light from a source of finite size casts a shadow with blurred edges

The occurrence of umbra and penumbra are common in astronomy. For example, during an eclipse of the sun by the moon, the moon passes between the sun and the earth. This is shown in Figure 3. There is a region, shown shaded in Figure 3, of umbra. If the earth moves relative to the moon along path A, then some parts of the earth will pass through the umbra and in those regions there will be a total eclipse of the sun. The regions surrounding the area of total eclipse will pass through the penumbra and will experience a partial eclipse since some part of the sun's disc will always be visible.

If, however, the earth moves relative to the moon along path B in Figure 3, no part of the earth will experience the umbra and the eclipse will everywhere be partial.

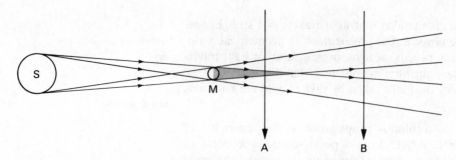

Figure 3   Eclipse of the sun S by the moon M. The shaded region shows the umbra. Along path A, the earth will experience a total solar eclipse as it passes through the umbra. Along path B the eclipse will be partial

2.2 The pinhole camera

The simplest optical instrument that can be made relies only on the principle of rectilinear propagation; this is the *pinhole camera*, shown in Figure 4. This is simply a box with a small hole in one side and a photographic plate on the opposite side. (You can construct one of these at home from an opened tin can; stretch some tracing paper over the open end and punch a hole in the centre of the closed end.)

pinhole camera

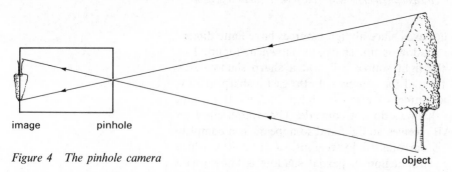

Figure 4   The pinhole camera

The disadvantage of this instrument is that the hole must be very small to produce a really sharp image. As a consequence the amount of light entering is very small. If the hole is made larger, more light enters but the image becomes blurred.

SAQ 1   (Objective 2)
Construct two ray diagrams for a pinhole camera, one with a small hole and one with a large hole. Use your diagram to explain why the image formed with a large hole is more blurred than one with a small hole.

3 REFLECTION

3.1 Reflection at a plane surface

It is a matter of common experience that if light is shone onto a polished plane surface it is reflected from that surface. This is shown in Figure 5. The description of the way the light is reflected is simplified by drawing in a normal PN to the mirror at the point P, where the light strikes the mirror (i.e. angle $N\hat{P}M = 90°$). We then define the angle between the incidence ray SP and the normal PN as the *angle of incidence* (i in Figure 5). The angle between the reflected ray PQ and the normal PN is called the *angle of reflection* (r in Figure 5).

angle of incidence
angle of reflection

Experimental observations allow two conclusions to be drawn and these are known as the *laws of reflection*. They state that:

laws of reflection

1 The incident ray, the reflected ray and the normal to the mirror at the point of incidence all lie in the same plane.

2 The angle of incidence is equal to the angle of reflection.

It is worth noting that if the first of these laws were not true then it would be impossible to draw ray diagrams such as Figure 5.

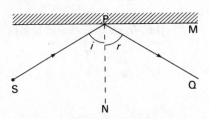

We can use the laws to determine the position of the image produced by a plane mirror. Look at Figure 6. An object O is placed in front of a plane mirror XY. We draw a ray OA, and draw in the normal to the mirror, AC. The angle of incidence of this ray is i_1 so, using the second law of reflection, the angle of reflection r_1 can be marked since $r_1 = i_1$. Hence the position of the reflected ray AB is fixed. By choosing a second ray OP and repeating this procedure the reflected ray PQ can be constructed.

Figure 5 Reflection at a plane surface. Light from source S strikes a mirror M. The angle i is the angle of incidence. Angle r is the angle of reflection. The non-reflecting side of the mirror is shown shaded

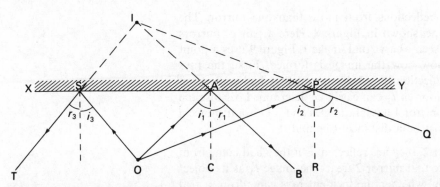

Figure 6 Locating the position of the image I of object O in front of a plane mirror by drawing in rays from the object to the mirror and constructing the reflected rays using the laws of reflection

You will observe that the reflected rays, AB and PQ in Figure 6, are diverging. However, if they are projected behind the mirror they intersect at a point I. In other words, the reflected rays appear to an observer as if they had come from point I. By drawing in a third ray, OST in Figure 6, it can be shown that *any* ray will be reflected in such a way that, when the reflected ray is projected behind the mirror, it passes through point I. Thus whereas all the incident rays originate at the object O, all reflected rays appear to originate from the point I. The point I is therefore the image of the point object O.

Because the image I lies somewhere behind the mirror and rays only *appear* to come from it, it is called a *virtual image*. As you will see later when we consider curved mirrors and lenses, some images can be thrown onto a screen; these are termed *real images*.

virtual image

real images

If, in Figure 6, you were to draw an incident ray that strikes the mirror at right angles, the angle of incidence would be zero and, from the second law of reflection, the angle of reflection would also be zero. In other words, the ray is reflected back along itself. So *the line joining object to image in a plane mirror must cross the mirror at right angles.*

We can now work out how far the image is behind the mirror. Figure 7 shows a ray normal to the mirror (OP) and a ray OQ making an angle of incidence i. All other lines were constructed as in Figure 6. It is not difficult to show that the angles take the values shown in Figure 7.

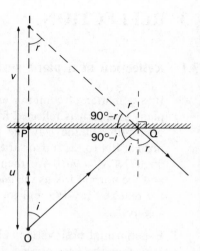

Figure 7 Locating the position of the image for a plane mirror

Let u be the distance of the object from the mirror and let v be the distance of the image behind the mirror. For triangle IPQ,

$$\tan r = \frac{PQ}{v}.$$

For triangle OPQ

$$\tan i = \frac{PQ}{u}.$$

But, from the second law of reflection, $i = r$, so $\tan i = \tan r$. Hence

$$\frac{PQ}{u} = \frac{PQ}{v}$$

so

$$u = v.$$

In other words, *the image is as far behind the mirror as the object is in front.*

3.2 The periscope

Many optical instruments use reflections from more than one mirror. The simplest example is the periscope, shown in Figure 8. Here a pair of mirrors are used so that an object O is seen as a virtual image I. Figure 9 uses a point object O and three rays to show how the image is formed. First, the rays encounter mirror 1 and after reflection they behave as if they had come from the image I_1. Note that the position of I_1 can easily be determined because the line joining O to I_1 must cross mirror 1 at right angles and if O is a distance d in front of mirror 1 then I_1 must be a distance d behind it.

When the rays encounter mirror 2, they are reflected as if they had come from image I_2. It is important to note that mirror 2 treats the image I_1 as its object since it has no way of 'knowing' whether the incident rays came from a real object or a virtual object. This is an important general principle that we shall be meeting again. Whenever an optical instrument contains a number of components, *the image produced by one component always acts as the object for the next component.* Thus in Figure 9, the line joining I_1 to I_2 will intersect mirror 2 at right angles and if image I_1 is a distance D in front of mirror 2 then the image I_2 will be a distance D behind mirror 2 as shown.

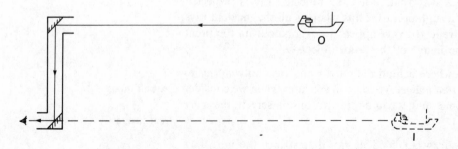

Figure 8 The simple periscope employing a pair of mirrors

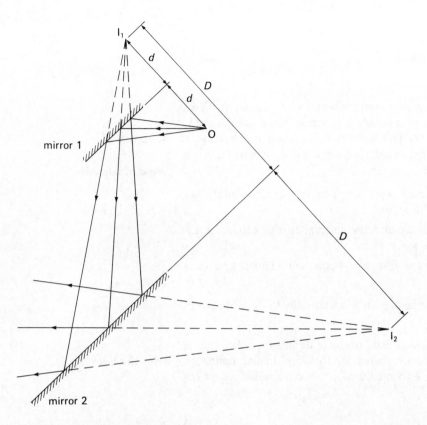

Figure 9   Ray diagram showing how the position of the final image in a periscope is determined

SAQ 2   (Objective 2)

A pair of parallel mirrors produce multiple reflections of an object be-tween them. Draw a ray diagrams showing two rays from the object to show where the final image appears to an observer after two reflections from each mirror (four reflections in total). (You will find this easier if you use squared paper.)

3.3   Summary of section 3

1   The laws of reflection state that

The incident ray, the reflected ray and the normal to the mirror at the point of incidence all lie in the same plane.

The angle of incidence is equal to the angle of reflection.

2   For reflection in a plane mirror, the line joining the object to the image intersects the mirror at right angles and the image is as far behind the mirror as the object is in front.

3   For optical instruments containing multiple components, the image pro-duced by one component acts as the object for the following component.

4   The image produced by a plane mirror is a virtual image.

You should now be able to attempt questions 571–5 in the *Problem Book*.

---

4 REFRACTION

4.1 The laws of refraction

When light passes from one medium into another it is bent as shown in Figure 10. An incident ray XO travelling in medium 1 passes a plane interface into medium 2 and is deflected along OY. This deflection is known as *refraction*. If the normal N to the interface is constructed, then angle i is known as the angle of incidence and angle r is the *angle of refraction*.

refraction

angle of refraction

The behaviour of light when refracted is governed by two experimental laws, known as the *laws of refraction*. These are:

laws of refraction

1 The incident ray, the refracted ray and the normal to the surface at the point of incidence all lie in the same plane.

2 For two given media, the ratio (sin i)/sin r is a constant. (This is known as Snell's law.)

Snell's law

The importance of the first of these laws is that it allows us to draw diagrams such as Figure 10.

The ratio (sin i)/(sin r), which is characteristic of the materials on either side of the interface, is known as the *refractive index* for those particular materials. For light travelling from medium 1 to medium 2, refractive index $_1n_2$ is defined as

refractive index

$$_1n_2 = \frac{\sin i}{\sin r} \tag{1}$$

Note that the refractive index is determined not just by the materials on either side of the interface, but also by the direction of the light. Thus the symbol $_1n_2$ means the refractive index for light travelling from medium 1 to medium 2. If we write $_2n_1$, this indicates light travelling from medium 2 to medium 1. This means that in Figure 10 the light would be in the reverse direction, so angle r becomes the angle of incidence and angle i becomes the angle of refraction. Hence

$$_2n_1 = \frac{\sin r}{\sin i}. \tag{2}$$

By comparing equations (1) and (2) you can see that

$$_1n_2 = \frac{1}{_2n_1}. \tag{3}$$

Refractive index data are tabulated for light travelling from a vacuum into the medium; such data are usually referred to as *absolute* refractive indices and typical examples are given in Table 1. For most practical purposes the refractive index for light travelling from air into the medium is the same as the absolute refractive index.

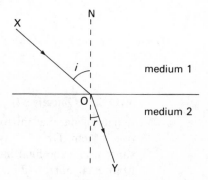

Figure 10 When light passes from one medium to another it is refracted. Line ON is the normal to the surface at the point of incidence, i is angle of incidence and r is angle of refraction

Table 1 Typical values of absolute refractive index (light travelling into the medium from a vacuum)

Material	Absolute refractive index
crown glass	1.48 to 1.61
ice	1.31
quartz	1.54
polystyrene	1.59
calcite	1.66
diamond	2.42
water	1.33

By way of a numerical example, suppose that the absolute refractive index of a sample of glass is 1.5. Then we may reasonably assume that the refractive index for light travelling from *air* into the glass will also be 1.5. From equation (3) the refractive index from glass into air will be $\frac{1}{1.5} = 0.67$. If light travelling in air strikes a plane air–glass interface at an angle of 45°, then the angle of refraction can be calculated from equation (1). We know that i is 45° and $_{air}n_{glass}$ is 1.5.

$$\sin r = \frac{\sin i}{_{air}n_{glass}},$$

so

$$\sin r = \frac{\sin 45°}{1.5}$$

$$= 0.471.$$

Hence $r = 28°$.

SAQ 3 (Objective 4)

If the refractive index $_{air}n_{quartz}$ is 1.54 calculate:

(a) the refractive index from quartz to air;

(b) the angle of refraction when the angle of incidence in air is 30°;

(c) the angle of refraction when the angle of incidence in quartz is 10°.

SAQ 4 (Objective 4)

Light is incident at an angle of 25° on one face of a parallel-sided glass block of refractive index 1.5 (air to glass). It emerges from the opposite face making an angle θ with the normal to the surface at the point of emergence. What is the angle θ?

4.2 Consequences of refraction

Suppose you were standing beside a pond looking at a fish swimming near the bottom. Because of refraction, light from the fish travels along the path shown in Figure 11. Since you are accustomed to light travelling in straight lines, you automatically interpret the light reaching your eyes as having come from the point F′ rather than F. In other words, the fish appears to be at an apparent depth A instead of its real depth R.

Not surprisingly, the real and apparent depths are related to refractive index. Writing $_{w}n_{a}$ as the refractive index for light travelling from water to air,

$$_{w}n_{a} = \frac{\sin i}{\sin r}, \tag{4}$$

where i and r are as in Figure 11. But angle $X\hat{F}Y$ is equal to angle i, so in triangle XFY

$$\sin i = \frac{XY}{FY}. \tag{5}$$

Similarly angle XF′Y must be equal to angle r, so in triangle XF′Y

$$\sin r = \frac{XY}{F'Y} \tag{6}$$

Combining equations (4), (5) and (6) gives

$$_{w}n_{a} = \frac{F'Y}{FY}. \tag{7}$$

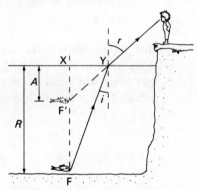

Figure 11   A fish F at a real depth R appears to be an apparent fish F′ at a depth A

43

Now, when angle i is small, say $10°$ or less, the following approximations can be made:

$$F'Y \approx A, \text{ apparent depth,}$$

and

$$FY \approx R, \text{ real depth.}$$

So

$$_wn_a = \frac{A}{R}$$

and since

$$_an_w = \frac{1}{_wn_a}$$

$$_an_w = \frac{R}{A}, \tag{8}$$

or, for *small angles of incidence and refraction,*

$$\frac{\text{Real depth}}{\text{Apparent depth}} = \text{refractive index from air to water.} \tag{9}$$

So if a fish is at the bottom of a pool 1.5 m deep, and the water has a refractive index from air to water of 1.33, the apparent depth is simply $\frac{1.5}{1.33}$ or 1.13 m.

SAQ 5   (Objective 5)

A plate glass window appears to be 10 mm thick. If the absolute refractive index of glass is 1.52, what is the real thickness of the window? (Assume small angles of incidence and refraction.)

SAQ 6   (Objective 5)

A mirror is formed by silvering one face of a block of glass of thickness 20 mm, and of refractive index 1.5. A speck of dust on the clear face forms an image in the opposite silvered face. How far apart do the speck of dust and its image appear to be to an outside observer? (Assume small angles.)

Now let us return to the fish swimming in a pond. What does the fish see as it looks towards the surface? Look at Figure 12. If it looks at point P, it receives light that was incident at an angle i at the surface. However, because i is greater than r distant objects will appear much closer.

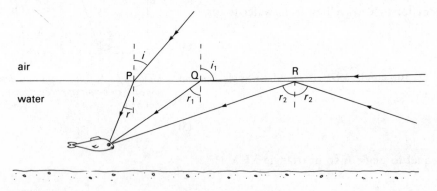

Figure 12   The occurrence of total internal reflection

More importantly, however, because the angle of incidence is greater than the angle of refraction, there is a point Q on the surface at which the incident light is just grazing the surface of the water. This enters the water with an angle of refraction r_1. So as far as the fish is concerned the whole of the world outside the pond is compressed into a circle on the surface, the limits of which are set by the angle r_1.

But what happens if the fish looks at an angle r_2 in Figure 12? The answer is that the surface behaves as a mirror and the fish will see reflections of objects in the pond.

The angle r_1 at which the surface of the pond begins to act as a mirror is called the *critical angle* and in Figure 12 this occurs when angle $i_1 = 90°$. So writing C for the critical angle, then since **critical angle**

$$_a n_w = \frac{\sin i_1}{\sin r_1}$$

then

$$_a n_w = \frac{1}{\sin C}. \tag{10}$$

Since the refractive index of water is 1.33, it follows from equation (10) that $\sin C = \frac{1}{1.33}$, and hence $C = 48.8°$.

The phenomenon by which light is reflected at the surface of a transparent medium is called *total internal reflection*. The important and useful property of **total internal reflection** total internal reflection is that *all* of the incident light is reflected, unlike reflection at a silvered surface where a small proportion is absorbed.

This property of total internal reflection is harnessed in many applications. The refractive index of glass is typically 1.5, so the critical angle (from equation 10) is 41.8°. Thus the mirrors in a periscope (see Figure 8) can be replaced with 45° prisms as shown in Figure 13(a). Light entering at A is normal to the glass surface ($i = 0$) and so continues undeflected. When it strikes the sloping surface at B, the angle of incidence is 45°, which is greater than the critical angle of 41.8° and so total internal reflection occurs. At surface C, the ray is again normal to the glass–air interface and so continues undeflected. Using prisms rather than mirrors produces a much brighter image.

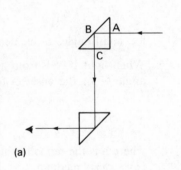

(a)

Another application, and one that is likely to assume increasing importance, is in fibre optics. This is illustrated in Figure 13(b). If light is shone into one end of a glass fibre it will suffer total internal reflection whenever it strikes the side of the fibre. So even though the fibre may follow a tortuous path, none of the light will escape through the sides of the fibre and the only losses will be light absorbed by the glass fibre.

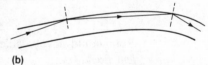

(b)

Figure 13 Uses of total internal reflection in (a) a periscope and (b) a glass fibre

SAQ 7 (Objective 6)

A spherical air bubble is attached to an underwater plant in an aquarium. The refractive index of the water in the tank is 1.3. Explain what the bubble looks like to an observer viewing it from the side of the tank.

SAQ 8 (Objective 6)

Figure 14 shows a section through a glass prism with angles as shown. A ray of light is incident as shown. Construct the path followed by this ray of light until it emerges from the prism if the refractive index of the glass is 1.5.

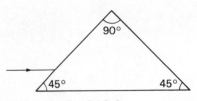

Figure 14   See SAQ 8

4.3 Summary of section 4

1 The laws of refraction are:

The incident ray, the refracted ray and the normal at the point of incidence all lie in the same plane.

The ratio $(\sin i)/\sin r$ is a constant.

2 For light travelling from medium 1 to medium 2 the refractive index $_1n_2$ is given by

$$_1n_2 = \frac{\sin i}{\sin r},$$

where i is the angle of incidence and r is the angle of refraction.

3 If $_1n_2$ is the refractive index for light travelling from medium 1 to medium 2 and $_2n_1$ is the refractive index for light travelling from medium 2 to medium 1, then

$$_1n_2 = \frac{1}{_2n_1}.$$

4 When an object is viewed through a material of absolute refractive index n, the real depth R is related to the apparent depth A by the equation

$$n = \frac{R}{A}$$

for small angles of incidence and refraction.

5 When light travels from a *more dense* to a *less dense* medium, the critical angle C for the onset of total internal reflection is given by

$$\sin C = \frac{1}{n},$$

where n is the refractive index for light travelling from the *less dense* to the *more dense* medium.

You should now be able to attempt questions 576–80 in the *Problem Book*.

---

5 REFRACTION IN THIN LENSES

5.1 The properties of lenses

A lens is an optical component, made of glass or some other transparent material, that has two spherical surfaces. In this respect a plane surface is regarded as a spherical surface of infinite radius. The line joining the centres of curvature of the two surfaces is called the *principal axis*.

principal axis

When the central portion of the lens is thicker than its edges, as in Figure 15(a), the lens is called a *convex lens*. If a beam of light parallel to the principal axis is incident on such a lens, it is brought to a focus at F; this is called the *principal focus* of the lens. Because such lenses cause parallel beams of light to converge they are also referred to as *converging lenses*. The lens, if symmetrical, could of course be reversed in the beam of light and the effect would be the same. There must therefore be a second focal point (F′ in Figure 15a) an equal distance from the lens as the distance of F.

convex lens

principal focus
converging lens

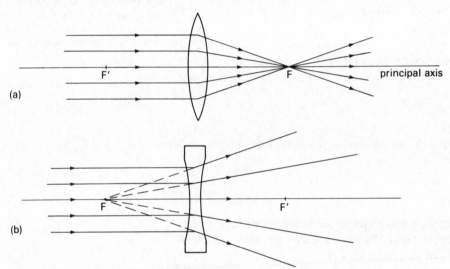

(a)

(b)

Figure 15   (a) Converging lens. (b) Diverging lens

When the central portion of the lens is thinner than the outer edges, as in Figure 15(b), the lens is called a *concave lens*. This possesses the property of causing a parallel beam of light to diverge, as shown in Figure 15(b), and for this reason such lenses are also referred to as *diverging lenses*. Note however that the refracted rays diverge from the point F on the same side as the incident beam. Again by reversing the lens it can be shown that a second focal point, F′, exists which is the same distance from the lens as F if the lens is symmetrical.

concave lens

diverging lens

The *focal length* of the lens is the distance between the focus and the centre of the lens. Because a converging lens has a real focus, it is usual to assign a positive value to focal length. In contrast, the focus of a diverging lens is virtual, and it is usual to assign a negative sign to the focal length. Thus a focal length of $+100$ mm implies a converging lens and a focal length of -100 mm implies a diverging lens. The importance of these signs will become clear in the later calculations.

focal length

5.2 Constructing the image produced by a lens

The image produced by an object in front of a lens can be located by constructing a ray diagram. It is assumed that the refraction takes place along the central plane of the lens, so when drawing ray diagrams we can represent the lenses by lines, as shown in Figure 16.

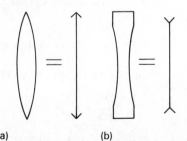

(a)   (b)

Figure 16   Symbols used for (a) converging lenses and (b) diverging lenses in ray diagrams

Ray diagram constructions for lenses always employ the same three rays. These are illustrated in Figure 17. They are:

(a) A ray parallel to the principal axis which, after refraction, passes through the principal focus (ray 1 in Figure 17).

(b) A ray through the centre of the lens, which continues undeflected (ray 2 in Figure 17).

(c) A ray incident through the other focus. This is refracted parallel to the principal axis (ray 3 in Figure 17).

For the converging lens of Figure 17(a) the image is real and inverted. For the diverging lens of Figure 17(b) the rays, after refraction, diverge as if they had come from I. So the image has to be constructed by projecting the refracted rays backwards. The image is therefore a virtual image.

An almost identical technique is used when constructing ray diagrams for spherical *mirrors*. The main difference is that instead of ray 2, which has no relevance for a mirror, we use a ray through the centre of curvature of the mirror. This is explained more fully in the audiovision tape *Calculations in Optics*, to which you will shortly be referred.

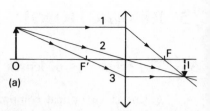

(a)

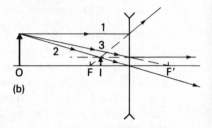

(b)

Figure 17   Ray diagrams showing the construction of the image I of an object O for (a) a converging lens and (b) a diverging lens. F is the principal focus, F' is the secondary focus

SAQ 9   (Objective 7)

A converging lens of focal length 100 mm forms an image of an object 200 mm in front of it. Draw a ray diagram to locate the position and size of the image.

SAQ 10   (Objective 7)

Repeat SAQ 9 but using a diverging lens of the same focal length.

5.3   The lens equation

For thin lenses there is a simple mathematical relationship between object distance, image distance and focal length. Figure 18 shows the construction of the image I, by a convex lens, of an object O. Let

  u be distance of object from the lens;

  v be distance of image from the lens;

  f be focal length of the lens.

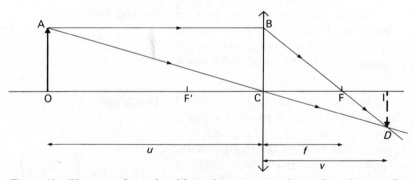

Figure 18   The image I, produced by a thin converging lens, of an object at O

In Figure 18, triangles OAC and CID are similar; so

$$\frac{OA}{ID} = \frac{OC}{IC}.$$

(11)

Triangles BCF and DIF are also similar, so

$$\frac{CB}{ID} = \frac{CF}{IF}.$$

(12)

But OA = CB so equation (12) becomes

$$\frac{OA}{ID} = \frac{CF}{IF}. \tag{13}$$

The left hand sides of equations (11) and (13) are identical, so the right hand sides of these equations must equal each other. So

$$\frac{OC}{IC} = \frac{CF}{IF} \tag{14}$$

Now substitute the distances u, v and f in equation (14) to give

$$\frac{u}{v} = \frac{f}{v - f}.$$

Hence

$$uv - uf = vf$$

or

$$vf + uf = uv.$$

Divide both sides by uvf to give

$$\frac{1}{u} + \frac{1}{v} = \frac{1}{f}. \tag{15}$$

Here then is a simple relationship between u, v and f which is known as the *lens equation*. We may also use Figure 18 to derive an expression for the magnification. Magnification m is defined by the equation

lens equation

$$m = \frac{\text{size of image}}{\text{size of object}}$$

$$= \frac{ID}{OA}. \tag{16}$$

But from equation (11)

$$\frac{ID}{OA} = \frac{IC}{OC} = \frac{v}{u}.$$

So, from equation (16),

$$m = \frac{v}{u}. \tag{17}$$

To illustrate the application of this equation suppose an object is 100 mm in front of a converging lens of focal length 20 mm. Find the position and size of the image. Here u is 100 mm and f is $+20$ mm, so

$$\frac{1}{u} + \frac{1}{v} = \frac{1}{f}$$

$$\frac{1}{v} = \frac{1}{f} - \frac{1}{u}$$

$$= \left(\frac{1}{20} - \frac{1}{100}\right) \text{mm}^{-1}$$

$$= \frac{80}{2000} \text{mm}^{-1}.$$

So

$$v = \frac{2000}{80} \text{mm}$$

$$= 25 \text{ mm}.$$

$$\text{Magnification} = \frac{v}{u} = \frac{25}{100} = \frac{1}{4}.$$

So the final image is 25 mm from the lens and is only one quarter of the size of the original object.

SAQ 11 (Objective 8)

An object of height 50 mm is placed 400 mm in front of a converging lens of focal length 100 mm. Calculate the position and size of the final image.

SAQ 12 (Objective 8)

An object is placed 30 mm in front of a converging lens of focal length 100 mm. Where does the final image appear?

The answer to SAQ 12 is a negative number and to see why, Figure 19 shows the ray diagram of the arrangement. As can be seen, the image is virtual; that is, it is produced by projecting the emergent rays backwards. So the emergent rays from the lens only appear to have come from the image I. It is invariably true that when the lens equation yields a negative value, the distance to which it refers represents a distance traversed by imaginary rays. You will recall that this was the reason why we assigned a negative value to the focal length of a diverging lens.

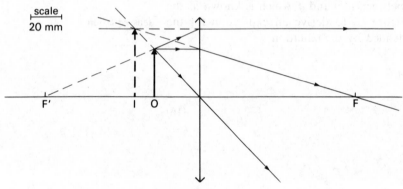

Figure 19   Production of a virtual image

These ideas are usually summarised by a *sign convention* for use with the lens equation. This says that distances traversed by real rays are positive. Distances traversed by imaginary rays are negative.

sign convention

To show how this is applied, suppose an object is placed 100 mm in front of a diverging lens of focal length 400 mm and let us calculate the position of the final image.

In this example $u = 100$ mm and $f = -400$ mm (negative because it is a diverging, or concave, lens).

$$\frac{1}{u} + \frac{1}{v} = \frac{1}{f}$$

so

$$\frac{1}{v} = \frac{1}{f} - \frac{1}{u}$$

$$= \left(-\frac{1}{400} - \frac{1}{100} \right) \text{mm}^{-1}$$

$$= -\frac{5}{400} \text{mm}^{-1}.$$

Hence

$$v = -\frac{400}{5}\,\text{mm}$$

$$= -80\,\text{mm}.$$

Since v is negative, the image is a virtual image. Note that when magnification is calculated from v/u we ignore the signs; we are interested only in the magnitudes of u and v.

SAQ 13 (Objective 8)

An object of height 20 mm is placed 50 mm in front of a converging lens of focal length 200 mm. Calculate the position and size of the image and state whether it is real or virtual.

SAQ 14 (Objective 8)

An object of height 10 mm is placed 25 mm in front of a diverging lens of focal length 50 mm. Calculate the position and size of the image and state whether it is real or virtual.

5.4 Lenses in combination

Many optical instruments employ more than one lens, so it is necessary to be able to calculate the position of the final image after the light has passed through a number of lenses. To illustrate the procedure used in such calculations let us consider the two-lens arrangement shown in Figure 20(a). A pair of converging lenses of focal lengths 100 mm and 50 mm are positioned 300 mm apart and an object is 250 mm in front of lens 1 as shown.

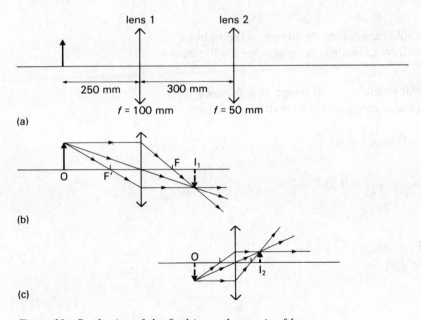

Figure 20 *Production of the final image by a pair of lenses*

The procedure is to perform calculations on each element in the order that the light from the object reaches them. The image produced by one element acts as the object for the next element.

So, in Figure 20(a), the first lens that the light encounters is lens 1. So we apply the lens equation to this element ignoring all other components. For lens 1:

$$u = 250\,\text{mm},$$

$$f = 100\,\text{mm}.$$

$$\frac{1}{u} + \frac{1}{v} = \frac{1}{f}$$

$$\frac{1}{v} = \frac{1}{f} - \frac{1}{u}$$

$$= \left(\frac{1}{100} - \frac{1}{250}\right) \text{mm}^{-1}$$

$$= \frac{3}{500} \text{mm}^{-1}$$

$$v = 167 \text{ mm}.$$

This is a real image and so will lie to the right of lens 1, a distance of 167 mm from it. We can confirm this by the ray diagram shown in Figure 20(b). Note that this need not be an accurate diagram – a sketch will usually be sufficient.

If the image produced by lens 1 is I_1 at a distance of 167 mm from lens 1, then this will be $(300 - 167)$ mm, or 133 mm, from lens 2. Image I_1 will now act as the object for lens 2. So, applying the lens equation to lens 2 we get:

$$u = 133 \text{ mm},$$

$$f = 50 \text{ mm}.$$

$$\frac{1}{v} = \frac{1}{f} - \frac{1}{u}$$

$$= \left(\frac{1}{50} - \frac{1}{133}\right) \text{mm}^{-1}$$

$$= \frac{133 - 50}{50 \times 133} \text{mm}^{-1}.$$

$$v = 80 \text{ mm}.$$

This again is a real image and we would expect it to lie 80 mm to the right of lens 2. Again we can confirm the result by drawing a ray diagram – see Figure 20(c).

So we find that this arrangement will produce a real image at a distance of 80 mm to the right of lens 2. We can also calculate the overall magnification:

$$\text{Magnification for lens 1, } m_1, = \frac{v}{u} = \frac{167}{250} = 0.67.$$

$$\text{Magnification in lens 2, } m_2, = \frac{v}{u} = \frac{80}{133} = 0.60.$$

So

$$\text{Overall magnification} = m_1 m_2$$

$$= 0.67 \times 0.60$$

$$= 0.402.$$

SAQ 15 (Objective 9)

An optical system consists of two identical converging lenses of focal length 100 mm placed 200 mm apart. An object is placed 300 mm in front of the system. Where will the final image appear? What is its magnification?

SAQ 16 (Objective 9)

An optical system consists of a converging lens of focal length 200 mm separated from a diverging lens of focal length 100 mm by a distance of 200 mm. An object is placed 1000 mm in front of the converging lens. Calculate the position and magnification of the final image.

You should now listen to the audiovision tape *Calculations in Optics*.

5.5 Summary of section 5

1 Ray diagrams are constructed using the following rays:

   (a) a ray incident parallel to the principal axis;

   (b) a ray through the centre of the lens;

   (c) a ray through the second focal point.

2 For any lens,

$$\frac{1}{u} + \frac{1}{v} = \frac{1}{f},$$

where

      u = distance from object to lens,

      v = distance from image to lens,

      f = focal length of lens.

3 The sign convention to use when applying the lens formula is that distances traversed by real rays are positive, and distances traversed by imaginary rays are negative. The focal lengths of converging lenses are positive; the focal lengths of diverging lenses are negative.

4 The magnification m produced by a lens is given by

$$m = \frac{v}{u}.$$

5 For combinations of lenses, the lens formula is applied in turn to the individual components; the image produced by one component acts as the object for the next.

You should now be able to attempt questions 581–90 in the *Problem Book*.

---

6 OPTICAL INSTRUMENTS

6.1 The human eye

Many optical instruments are designed so that the final image is viewed directly by the eye, and so it is necessary to know the requirements, and limitations, of the eye so that instruments can be designed and set up to produce an image that can be viewed comfortably.

Figure 21 shows a horizontal section through the human eye. Essentially, the eye is an almost spherical container with a tough outer wall (the sclerotic). It is divided into two chambers. The front chamber is bounded by the cornea and the front face of the lens and is filled with a watery fluid known as aqueous humour. The rear chamber is bounded by the rear surface of the lens and the nerve-endings which form the retina, and this chamber is filled with a jelly-like substance called the vitreous humour. The whole of the rear chamber is coated with a layer of black tissue (the choroid) which absorbs any light passing through the retina.

Optically the eye produces images on the retina by refraction through the cornea and the lens, with the cornea playing the major role. The lens can be regarded as the fine focusing adjustment since its focal length is adjustable by the ciliary muscle, to which it is attached. When this muscle stretches the lens, the radius of curvature of the lens surface is increased and the focal length increases. The process of adjusting the eye to focus on objects at different distances is called *accommodation*. **accommodation**

In discussing the optical performance of the eye it is usual to define two terms. The *far point* is the point on which the fully relaxed eye is focused. In a normal **far point** eye the far point is at infinity; that is, parallel light entering the eye is focused on the retina. The *near point* is the point at which the fully accommodated eye **near point** is focused and represents the closest distance at which an object can be comfortably viewed. In a normal eye the near point is about 250 mm from the eye.

Two of the commonest eye defects are short sight (*myopia*) and long sight **myopia** (*hypermetropia*). In the myopic eye, the far point is not at infinity, as shown in **hypermetropia** Figure 22(a). The defect can be counteracted by putting a diverging lens in

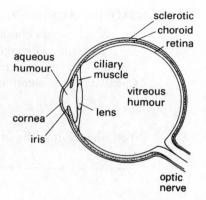

Figure 21   Horizontal section through the human eye

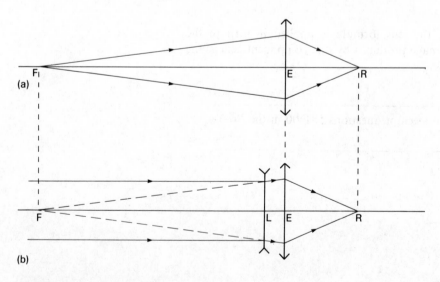

Figure 22   In the myopic eye the far point is not at infinity. (a) For the fully relaxed eye an object at the far point F is focused by the eye E onto the retina R. (b) When the defect is corrected using a diverging lens L, light from infinity produces a virtual image at the far point onto which the eye can comfortably focus

front of the eye. This produces an image at the far point of an object at infinity. Since parallel light focuses at the focal point of a lens, it follows in Figure 22(b) that the distance LF must be the focal length of the spectacle lens L needed to correct the defect. Thus, for example, if the far point is situated 10 m from the eye and the spectacle lens is typically 10 mm in front of the eye, the correct focal length of the diverging lens should be $(10 - 0.01)$ m $= 9.99$ m.

In hypermetropia, the near point is too far from the eye so that whereas it can comfortably focus on distant objects, it cannot comfortably focus on close objects, as shown in Figure 23(a). This defect is corrected by a converging spectacle lens (Figure 23b). When an object is placed at the correct near point, N′, (say 250 mm) the spectacle lens produces a virtual image at the actual near point, N. This the eye can see comfortably.

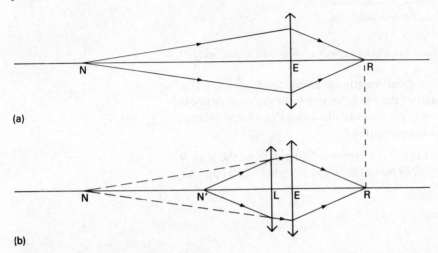

(a)

(b)

Figure 23 (a) *In hypermetropia, the near point* N *is too far from the eye* E. (b) *It is corrected using a converging lens so that an object at the correct near point* N′ *produces a virtual image at* N *which the eye then focuses on the retina* R

It is not difficult to calculate the focal length of the required spectacle lens using the lens formula. Suppose that an eye has a near point a distance of 500 mm away and a spectacle lens 10 mm from the eye is to provide a correct near point at 250 mm. The required lens has to take an object at a distance of $(250 - 10)$ mm, or 240 mm, and produce a *virtual* image at a distance of $(500 - 10)$ mm, or 490 mm. So

$u = 240$ mm,

$v = -490$ mm.

Hence, by applying the lens formula,

$$\frac{1}{u} + \frac{1}{v} = \frac{1}{f}$$

$$\frac{1}{f} = \left(\frac{1}{240} - \frac{1}{490}\right) mm^{-1}.$$

$f = 470$ mm.

SAQ 17 (Objective 10)

A short-sighted person has a far point at 3 m from the eye and a near point 250 mm from the eye. Calculate:

(a) the focal length of the lens needed to correct the myopia if the lens is 10 mm from the eye;

(b) the position of the corrected near point when the person is wearing the spectacles.

6.2 The magnifying glass

Figure 19 showed that if an object is placed between a converging lens and its focal point, a magnified virtual image is produced. This effect is the basis of the *magnifying glass* shown in Figure 24.

magnifying glass

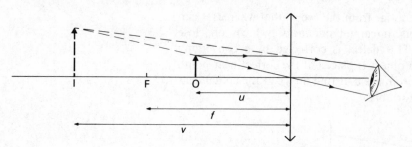

Figure 24   The magnifying glass. An object at O produces a magnified virtual image I

Suppose a magnifying lens has a focal length of 30 mm and it is used to produce an image at the near point of the eye (250 mm from the eye). Suppose that the eye is 10 mm from the lens. Where must the object be placed relative to the lens and what will be the magnification?

The image must occur a distance of (250 − 10) mm = 240 mm from the lens. It will be a virtual image, so $v = -240$ mm. The focal length $f = 30$ mm. So, applying the lens equation,

$$\frac{1}{u} + \frac{1}{v} = \frac{1}{f}$$

$$\frac{1}{u} = \frac{1}{f} - \frac{1}{v}$$

$$= \left(\frac{1}{30} - \frac{1}{240}\right) \text{mm}^{-1}.$$

$u = 34.3$ mm.

So the object must be 34.3 mm from the lens. Magnification is therefore

$$m = \frac{v}{u} = \frac{240}{34.3} = 7.$$

The image is therefore magnified 7 times.

SAQ 18   (Objective 11)

Calculate the focal length of the magnifying glass needed to produce an image with a magnification of 10 at the near point of the eye of an observer. The near point is 250 mm from the eye and the eye is held 20 mm away from the lens.

The limitation on the use of the magnifying glass as a means of producing enlarged images is well illustrated by the answer to SAQ 18. For quite modest magnifications the focal length of the lens required is very short and the image distance becomes critical. For greater magnifications than about 10 these values become so small that its use is impractical, and the single lens system is replaced by a multicomponent system – the *compound microscope*.

compound microscope

6.3 The compound microscope

The principle of the compound microscope is illustrated in Figure 25. The object O is placed just outside the focus F'_o of a converging lens known as the *objective*, and this lens produces a real image I_o which falls within the focal

objective

length of a second converging lens, or *eyepiece*. The resultant image is a magnified, virtual image, I_e. In use the final image would be formed so that it falls at the near point of the eye.

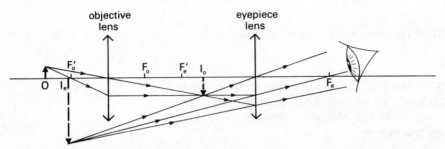

Figure 25   The simple compound microscope

The essential difference between this arrangement and the single magnifying lens is that the magnification is carried out in two stages. When an object is placed at a point lying between f and $2f$ in front of a converging lens of focal length f, the resulting real image is always magnified. If the image produced by such an arrangement falls within the focal length of a second converging lens, the final virtual image will again be magnified. Thus if the magnification at the objective is m_o and the magnification at the eyepiece is m_e, the overall magnification is the product of these; that is, $m_o m_e$. Thus with quite modest magnifications at each lens, the overall magnification can be quite significant.

For example, suppose that a simple compound microscope such as that in Figure 25 has an objective of focal length 30 mm, an eyepiece of focal length 60 mm, and that the lenses are separated by a distance of 378 mm. If the object is placed 33 m in front of the objective, what is the overall magnification of the instrument?

We simply apply the lens formula in turn to the objective and the eyepiece. So, for the objective, $u = 33$ mm, and $f = 30$ mm.

$$\frac{1}{u} + \frac{1}{v} = \frac{1}{f}$$

$$\frac{1}{v} = \left(\frac{1}{f} - \frac{1}{u}\right) \text{mm}^{-1}$$

$$= \left(\frac{1}{30} - \frac{1}{33}\right) \text{mm}^{-1}.$$

$$v = 330 \text{ mm}.$$

Magnification at the objective m_o is given by

$$m_o = \frac{v}{u} = \frac{330}{33} = 10.$$

The image produced by the objective is 330 mm from the objective, so it must be $(378 - 330)$ mm, or 48 mm, from the eyepiece. So, for the eyepiece,

$u = 48$ mm, and $f = 60$ mm.

$$\frac{1}{u} + \frac{1}{v} = \frac{1}{f}$$

$$\frac{1}{v} = \frac{1}{f} - \frac{1}{u}$$

$$= \left(\frac{1}{60} - \frac{1}{48}\right) \text{mm}^{-1}.$$

$$v = -240 \text{ mm}.$$

The negative sign indicates a virtual image. The magnification produced by the eyepiece m_e is given by

$$m_e = \frac{v}{u} = \frac{240}{48} = 5.$$

So the overall magnification M of the instrument is $m_o m_e = 10 \times 5 = 50$.

SAQ 19 (Objective 11)

A simple compound microscope has an objective lens of focal length 40 mm at a distance of 572 mm from an eyepiece of focal length 60 mm. An object is placed 43.3 mm from the objective. What is the overall magnification produced by this system?

SAQ 20 (Objective 11)

A simple compound microscope has an overall magnification of 96 when the final image is a distance of 250 mm from the eyepiece and when the magnification in the eyepiece is 8. The focal length of the objective is 30 mm and the focal length of the eyepiece is 45 mm. Calculate:

(a) the position of the object relative to the objective;
(b) the separation of the lenses.

6.4 The general approach to analysing optical instruments

The analysis technique used in section 6.3 is a general technique and can be used for optical systems containing any number of elements. The important point to remember is that the elements must always be treated in the order in which the light reaches them from the object, and the image produced by one element always acts as the object for the next element. If you follow this rule rigorously then the lens equation when used repeatedly will allow you to calculate the position of the final image. The only feature of the calculations that you must be constantly on guard against is the production of virtual images (or objects).

6.5 Summary of section 6

1 The far point is the point at which the human eye is focused when fully relaxed; in the normal eye it is at infinity.

2 The near point is the point at which the human eye is focused when fully accommodated; in a normal eye it is approximately 250 mm from the eye.

3 In myopia (short sight) the far point is not at infinity; it is corrected with a diverging lens.

4 In hypermetropia (long sight) the near point is too far from the eye. It is corrected with a converging lens.

5 All optical systems can be analysed using the formulae

$$\frac{1}{u} + \frac{1}{v} = \frac{1}{f} \quad \text{and} \quad m = \frac{v}{u}$$

where u is object distance, v is image distance, f is focal length of the component and m is magnification in the component.

6 In multicomponent systems, the elements are analysed in the order in which light encounters them, with the image from one component acting as the object for the next component.

You should now be able to attempt questions 591–5 in the *Problem Book*.

ANSWERS TO SELF-ASSESSMENT QUESTIONS

SAQ 1

The two ray diagrams are shown in Figure 26. In (a), where the pinhole is small, the image is relatively sharp. In (b), where the hole is large, rays from point P on the object may enter the camera anywhere between X and Y so the image of point P will be spread over the region BD on the screen. Similarly the image of point Q on the object will be spread over the region AC. Note that in the region BC, both top and bottom of the object will produce an image; so with a hole of this size the image would be so blurred that it would probably be unidentifiable.

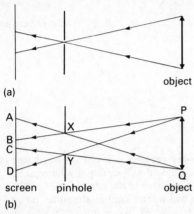

Figure 26   See SAQ 1

SAQ 2

The ray diagram is shown in Figure 27 and the images I_1, I_2, I_3 and I_4 show the images produced by successive reflections.

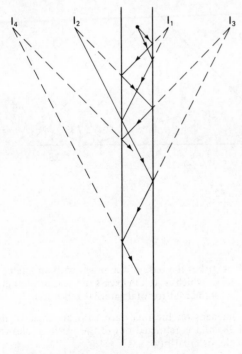

Figure 27   See SAQ 2

SAQ 3

(a) $_1n_2 = \dfrac{1}{_2n_1}$ (from equation 3).

So, writing $_an_q$ for $_{air}n_{quartz}$ and $_qn_a$ for $_{quartz}n_{air}$,

$$_qn_a = \frac{1}{_an_q}$$

$$= \frac{1}{1.54}$$

$$= 0.65.$$

(b) $_an_q = \dfrac{\sin i}{\sin r}$

so

$$\sin r = \frac{\sin i}{_an_q}.$$

We are told that $i = 30°$ and $_an_q = 1.54$, so

$$\sin r = \frac{\sin 30°}{1.54}$$

$$= 0.3247$$

$$r = 19°.$$

(c) $_qn_a = \dfrac{\sin i}{\sin r}$

so

$$\sin r = \frac{\sin i}{_qn_a}.$$

We are told that i is $10°$, and we know that $_qn_a$ is $1/_an_q$, which is $\frac{1}{1.54}$ or 0.65, so

$$\sin r = \frac{\sin 10°}{0.65}$$

$$= 0.2672$$

$$r = 15.5°.$$

SAQ 4

The arrangement is shown in Figure 28. Let i be the angle of incidence at the first surface and let r be the angle of refraction. Now, because the sides of the block are parallel, the angle of incidence on the second face will also be r. The angle of emergence θ is as shown.

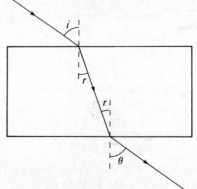

Figure 28   See SAQ 4

So at the first interface

$$_a n_g = \frac{\sin i}{\sin r}.$$

At the second interface

$$_g n_a = \frac{\sin r}{\sin \theta}.$$

But $_a n_g = \frac{1}{_g n_a}$, so

$$\frac{\sin i}{\sin r} = \frac{\sin \theta}{\sin r}.$$

Hence

$$\theta = i,$$

so

$$\theta = 25°.$$

SAQ 5

Refractive index $n = \dfrac{\text{real depth } R}{\text{apparent depth } A}$,

so

$$R = nA.$$

Here $n = 1.52$ and $A = 10$ mm, so

$$R = nA$$
$$= (1.52 \times 10) \text{ mm}$$
$$= 15.2 \text{ mm}.$$

SAQ 6

Figure 29(a) shows the way the image is produced, at an apparent depth A. As far as the observer is concerned, precisely the same image at an apparent depth A would be produced if the speck of dust were on the far side of an unsilvered block of twice the thickness. See Figure 29(b).

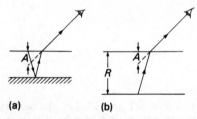

(a)　　　　**(b)**

Figure 29　See SAQ 6

Now, referring to Figure 29(b),

Refractive index $n = \dfrac{\text{real depth } R}{\text{apparent depth } A}$.

So

$$A = \frac{R}{n}.$$

Now, $R = 20$ mm $\times 2 = 40$ mm, and $n = 1.5$, so

$$A = \frac{40}{1.5} \text{ mm}$$
$$= 26.66 \text{ mm}.$$

Referring to Figure 29(a), A is the distance between the speck of dust and its image, so the separation of dust and image is 26.66 mm.

SAQ 7

Look at Figure 30. If the observer looks in the central region of the bubble (e.g. point A), the angle θ is less than the critical angle (of 50°) and so the observer will be able to see through the bubble.

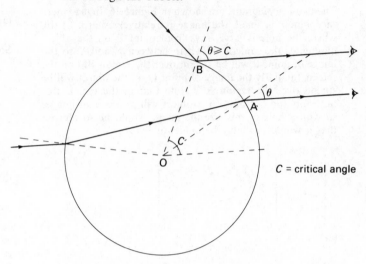

Figure 30　See SAQ 7

However, as the observer moves his eye towards the edge of the bubble, the angle θ will eventually be equal to the critical angle and from here to the edge of the bubble, total internal reflection will occur. That is, the outer part of the bubble will appear silvered like a mirror. So the central part of the bubble will be transparent but the outer edges will behave like mirrors.

SAQ 8

See Figure 31. The angle of incidence at the first surface is 45°. So the angle of refraction r is given by

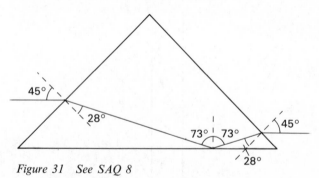

Figure 31　See SAQ 8

$$1.5 = \frac{\sin 45°}{\sin r}.$$

So

$$r = 28°.$$

The ray then strikes the base of the prism with an angle of incidence of 73°, which is well in excess of the critical angle. It is therefore subjected to total internal reflection.

It then is incident on the final face with an angle of incidence of 28° and is refracted out of the prism as shown, parallel to the original ray.

SAQ 9

The ray diagrams is shown in Figure 32. As can be seen, the image is an equal distance on the other side of the lens and is the same size as the object. The image is also real.

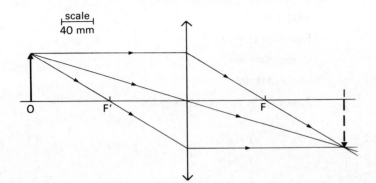

Figure 32   See SAQ 9

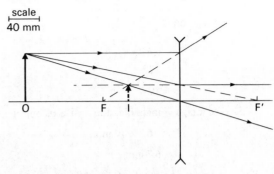

Figure 33   See SAQ 10

SAQ 10

The ray diagram is shown in Figure 33. The image I is a virtual, diminished image on the same side of the lens as the object.

SAQ 11

This is a straightforward application of the lens equation:

$$\frac{1}{u} + \frac{1}{v} = \frac{1}{f},$$

where $u = 400$ mm and $f = +100$ mm. So

$$\frac{1}{v} = \frac{1}{f} - \frac{1}{u}$$

$$= \left(\frac{1}{100} - \frac{1}{400}\right) \text{mm}^{-1}$$

$$= \frac{3}{400} \text{mm}^{-1}$$

$$v = \frac{400}{3} \text{mm}$$

$$= 133 \text{ mm}.$$

$$\text{Magnification} = \frac{v}{u}$$

$$= \frac{133}{400}$$

$$= 0.33.$$

SAQ 12

$$\frac{1}{u} + \frac{1}{v} = \frac{1}{f}$$

so

$$\frac{1}{v} = \frac{1}{f} - \frac{1}{u}.$$

From the question, $u = 30$ mm and $f = +100$ mm. So

$$\frac{1}{v} = \left(\frac{1}{100} - \frac{1}{30}\right) \text{mm}^{-1}.$$

$$= -\frac{7}{300} \text{mm}^{-1}$$

$$v = -42.9 \text{ mm}.$$

See the following main text for an explanation of the minus sign.

SAQ 13

We are given $u = 50$ mm and $f = 200$ mm.

$$\frac{1}{u} + \frac{1}{v} = \frac{1}{f},$$

so

$$\frac{1}{v} = \frac{1}{f} - \frac{1}{u}$$

$$= \left(\frac{1}{200} - \frac{1}{50}\right) \text{mm}^{-1}$$

$$= -\frac{3}{200} \text{mm}^{-1}.$$

So

$$v = -\frac{200}{3} \text{mm}$$

$$= -66.7 \text{ mm}.$$

$$\text{Magnification} = \frac{v}{u}$$

$$= \frac{66.7}{50}$$

$$= 1.33.$$

$$\text{Size} = \text{magnification} \times \text{object size}$$

$$= (1.33 \times 20) \text{ mm}$$

$$= 26.6 \text{ mm}.$$

So final image is virtual, of size 26.6 mm, located 66.7 mm from the lens.

SAQ 14

We are given that $u = 25$ mm and $f = -50$ mm.

$$\frac{1}{u} + \frac{1}{v} = \frac{1}{f}$$

so

$$\frac{1}{v} = \frac{1}{f} - \frac{1}{u}$$

$$= \left(-\frac{1}{50} - \frac{1}{25}\right) \text{mm}^{-1}$$

$$= -\frac{3}{50} \text{mm}^{-1}.$$

$$v = -\frac{50}{3} \text{mm}$$

$$= -16.7 \text{ mm}.$$

Magnification $= \dfrac{v}{u}$

$$= \dfrac{16.7}{25}$$

$$= 0.67.$$

Size of image = magnification × size of object

$$= 0.67 \times 10 \text{ mm}$$

$$= 6.7 \text{ mm}.$$

So final image is virtual, of size 6.7 mm located 16.7 mm from the lens.

SAQ 15

For refraction at the first lens

$u = 300 \text{ mm}$

$f = 100 \text{ mm}.$

Applying the lens formula,

$$\dfrac{1}{u} + \dfrac{1}{v} = \dfrac{1}{f}$$

$$\dfrac{1}{v} = \dfrac{1}{f} - \dfrac{1}{u}$$

$$= \left(\dfrac{1}{100} - \dfrac{1}{300} \right) \text{mm}^{-1}$$

$$= \dfrac{2}{300} \text{ mm}^{-1}.$$

$v = 150 \text{ mm}.$

This is a real image and so will appear on the opposite side of the lens to the object; i.e. it will be between the lens combination a distance of 150 mm from lens 1, or 50 mm from lens 2. This image will now act as the object for lens 2, so

$u = 50 \text{ mm},$

$f = 100 \text{ mm}.$

Applying the lens equation to lens 2,

$$\dfrac{1}{u} + \dfrac{1}{v} = \dfrac{1}{f}$$

$$\dfrac{1}{v} = \dfrac{1}{f} - \dfrac{1}{u}$$

$$= \left(\dfrac{1}{100} - \dfrac{1}{50} \right) \text{mm}^{-1}$$

$$= -\dfrac{1}{100} \text{ mm}^{-1}.$$

$v = -100 \text{ mm}.$

This is a virtual image; that is, the rays from lens 2 are diverging and so must be projected back to produce the image. The final image therefore will also lie between the lenses – you can check this by sketching the ray diagram.

Magnification by lens 1, $m_1, = \dfrac{v}{u} = \dfrac{150}{300} = 0.5.$

Magnification by lens 2, $m_2, = \dfrac{v}{u} = \dfrac{100}{50} = 2.$

Overall magnification $= m_1 m_2 = 0.5 \times 2 = 1.$

So the final image is the same size as the object.

SAQ 16

For the first lens:

$u = 1000 \text{ mm},$

$f = 200 \text{ mm}.$

Applying the lens equation to lens 1,

$$\dfrac{1}{u} + \dfrac{1}{v} = \dfrac{1}{f}$$

$$\dfrac{1}{v} = \dfrac{1}{f} - \dfrac{1}{u}$$

$$= \left(\dfrac{1}{200} - \dfrac{1}{1000} \right) \text{mm}^{-1}$$

$$= \dfrac{5 - 1}{1000} \text{ mm}^{-1}.$$

$v = 250 \text{ mm}.$

This is a real image and so it appears on the opposite side of the lens from the object. Now there is a slight problem. The components of the system are only 200 mm apart, so this image is also to the right of lens 2; that is, it is a *virtual object* for lens 2. So for lens 2,

$u = -(250 - 200) \text{ mm} = -50 \text{ mm}.$

$f = -100 \text{ mm}$ (minus because it is a diverging lens).

So, applying the lens equation to lens 2 gives,

$$\dfrac{1}{v} = \dfrac{1}{f} - \dfrac{1}{u}$$

$$= \left(-\dfrac{1}{100} + \dfrac{1}{50} \right) \text{mm}^{-1}$$

$$= \dfrac{1}{100} \text{ mm}^{-1}.$$

$v = 100 \text{ mm}.$

This is a real image and so will appear to the right of the diverging lens a distance of 100 mm from it.

Magnification in lens 1, $m_1, = \dfrac{v}{u} = \dfrac{250}{1000} = \dfrac{1}{4} = 0.25.$

Magnification in lens 2, $m_2, = \dfrac{v}{u} = \dfrac{100}{50} = 2.$

Overall magnification $= m_1 m_2$

$$= 0.25 \times 2$$

$$= 0.5.$$

The final image is half the size of the object.

SAQ 17

(a) If the far point is 3 m from the eye, then it is

$(3 - 0.01) \text{ mm} = 2.99 \text{ m}$

from the correction lens. The lens must therefore take parallel light and focus it at a distance of 2.99 m from the eye. That is, the diverging lens used must be of focal length 2.99 m.

(b) If an object is so placed that its image is at the *uncorrected* near point of the eye, the image will be at a distance of

$-(250 - 10) \text{ mm} = -240 \text{ mm}$

from the lens. This distance is negative because it is a virtual image. To calculate the new near point, we need to calculate the object distance that will produce this image distance. So,

$$v = -240 \text{ mm}$$
$$f = -2.99 \text{ m} = -2990 \text{ mm}.$$

Apply the lens equation,

$$\frac{1}{u} + \frac{1}{v} = \frac{1}{f}$$
$$\frac{1}{u} = \frac{1}{f} - \frac{1}{v}$$
$$= \left(-\frac{1}{2990} + \frac{1}{240}\right) \text{mm}^{-1}$$
$$= 3.83 \times 10^{-3} \text{ mm}^{-1}.$$

So $u = 261 \text{ mm}$.

The new near point will be 261 mm from the lens, or 271 mm from the eye. That is, the near point has moved further from the eye.

SAQ 18

$$\text{Magnification} = m = \frac{v}{u} = 10.$$

But $v = -(250 - 10) \text{ mm} = -240 \text{ mm}$. So, ignoring the minus sign which has no meaning in the magnification equation,

$$u = \frac{v}{10} = \frac{240}{10} \text{ mm} = 24 \text{ mm}.$$

Now we apply the lens equation:

$$\frac{1}{u} + \frac{1}{v} = \frac{1}{f}.$$

We know that $u = 24 \text{ mm}$ and $v = -240 \text{ mm}$, so

$$\frac{1}{f} = \left(\frac{1}{24} - \frac{1}{240}\right) \text{mm}^{-1}$$

and so $f = 26.7 \text{ mm}$.

SAQ 19

For the objective lens,

$$u = 43.3 \text{ mm},$$
$$f = 40 \text{ mm}.$$

Applying the lens equation:

$$\frac{1}{u} + \frac{1}{v} = \frac{1}{f}$$
$$\frac{1}{v} = \frac{1}{f} - \frac{1}{u}$$
$$= \left(\frac{1}{40} - \frac{1}{43.3}\right) \text{mm}^{-1}.$$
$$v = 524.8 \text{ mm}.$$

$$\text{Magnification at objective, } m_o, = \frac{v}{u} = \frac{524.8}{43.3} = 12.1.$$

The image produced by the objective is 524.8 mm from the objective and so it must be $(572 - 524.8) \text{ mm}$, or 47.2 mm from the eyepiece. So for the eyepiece,

$$u = 47.2 \text{ mm},$$
$$f = 60 \text{ mm}.$$

Applying the lens equation,

$$\frac{1}{u} + \frac{1}{v} = \frac{1}{f}$$
$$\frac{1}{v} = \frac{1}{f} - \frac{1}{u}$$
$$= \left(\frac{1}{60} - \frac{1}{47.2}\right) \text{mm}^{-1}$$
$$v = -221.3 \text{ mm}.$$

$$\text{Magnification by the eyepiece, } m_e, = \frac{v}{u} = \frac{221.3}{47.2} = 4.7.$$

So

Overall magnification $m_o m_e = 12.1 \times 4.7 = 56.9$.

SAQ 20

For the eyepiece,

$$\text{Magnification } m_e = \frac{v}{u},$$

so

$$u = \frac{v}{m_e}.$$

But $m_e = 8$ and $v = 250 \text{ mm}$, so

$$u = \frac{250}{8} \text{ mm} = 31.25 \text{ mm}.$$

For the objective, the magnification m_o must be $(96/12) = 8$. Now

$$m_o = \frac{v}{u}$$

so

$$v = m_o u = 8u.$$

Apply the lens equation for the objective:

$$\frac{1}{u} + \frac{1}{v} = \frac{1}{f}$$
$$\frac{1}{u} + \frac{1}{8u} = \frac{1}{f}$$
$$\frac{9}{8u} = \frac{1}{f}$$
$$u = \frac{9 \times f}{8} = \frac{9 \times 30}{8} \text{ mm} = 33.75 \text{ mm}.$$

So, in answer to (a), the object is 33.75 mm from the objective. To find the answer to (b), the separation of the lenses, the required distance is the sum of the image distance for the objective and the object distance for the eyepiece.

For the objective, $v = 8u$, as we have seen. So

$$v = 8 \times 33.75 \text{ mm}$$
$$= 270 \text{ mm}.$$

For the eyepiece, object distance is 31.25 mm. So the separation of the lenses is

$$(270 + 31.25) \text{ mm} = 301.25 \text{ mm}.$$

T281 BASIC PHYSICAL SCIENCE FOR TECHNOLOGY